Laycock, George
Big Nick

DATE DUE

FT JO F 9 6 6 -79	
JUNCT A 1 6 6'80	
DORR G 9 10'81	
BIG S F 1 - 18'82	
SEIAD C 3 4 82	
BIG S 1 0 8'84	
2-8-85	

The reader is introduced to the Great Smoky Mountains National Park as he follows the escapades of the biggest black bear, Nick, in this accurate and sensitive biographical story. How bears live in the wild, moving through the natural pattern of life while skirting the edges of civilization, "where man either hunts him with guns or spoils him with hand-outs," is told simply with understanding and sensitivity.

BIG NICK

The Story of a Remarkable Black Bear

BIG NICK

The Story of a Remarkable Black Bear

by GEORGE LAYCOCK

Illustrated by NANCY GROSSMAN

W · W · NORTON & COMPANY · INC · NEW YORK

Books by GEORGE LAYCOCK

Big Nick, the Story of a Remarkable Black Bear

Whitetail, the Story of a White-tailed Deer

Never Trust a Cowbird

Never Pet a Porcupine

Text Copyright © 1967 by George Laycock

Illustrations Copyright © 1967 by W. W. Norton & Company, Inc.

Library of Congress Catalog Card No. AC 67-10320

Published simultaneously in Canada by
George J. McLeod Limited, Toronto

Printed in the United States of America

3 4 5 6 7 8 9 0

Preface *Bears and People*

When the country was younger, black bears roamed the timberlands throughout much of North America. There they found the nuts, berries, and small creatures that have always provided their natural foods. Their wild enemies were few, but as settlers advanced across the country, bears faced new dangers. Fire and ax destroyed their habitats while guns and traps reduced their numbers steadily.

The black bear is shy and elusive. He stays out of trouble by staying out of sight. More often than not, the bear's acute hearing and sensitive nose detect man's approach. Long before the human sees the bear, *Ursus americanus* has stopped abruptly in his woodland wanderings, risen briefly to his hind feet, then dropped to all fours, and dashed off in the opposite direction. In his escape he may attain speeds of twenty-eight miles an hour.

Wherever bears appear on the human scene, however, people are likely to declare a state of emergency. Even a small bear can cause panic by bumbling into a village street. Recently a bewildered sixty pound yearling wandered into a western town. Armed men quickly surrounded the cub and destroyed it.

In another town a businessman slipped into a bear costume as a holiday promotion stunt. When nobody was looking, he climbed a tree in the town square and perched there to see what would happen. It seemed harmless enough until a citizen in the growing crowd called the sheriff's office.

1

Shortly a patrol car arrived at the scene. A deputy rushed from the car and pointed his rifle at the treed creature. He noticed just in time, as he sighted down the rifle barrel, that the "bear" was wearing street shoes.

Because black bears are adaptable, they have survived the increasing encroachment of humans on the land. Forest-fire protection and hunting regulations have helped bears return to areas from which they were once eliminated.

But most people who see wild bears today encounter them in a few of the larger national parks, especially Yellowstone, Yosemite, and the Great Smoky Mountains. Yellowstone is home to an estimated five hundred black bears and the Great Smoky Mountains National Park has perhaps three hundred. "The reason there seems to be more," explains one National Park naturalist, "is that in the summertime most of our bears are down along the highways begging."

As visitors to the national parks have learned, black bears are not always really black as they are in the Great Smoky Mountains. In some western parks bears come in a variety of color phases. Yellowstone visitors encounter black bears, blond bears, and cinnamon-colored bears, sometimes in the same family of cubs.

In the parks the bears seem to have learned that they are protected. They have also learned to beg for food. Some have even found that they can stop a line of traffic by sitting in the middle of the highway. Such park bears have sacrificed independence in exchange for man's cookies, fruit, and gum drops.

There exists, however, between park bears and their human admirers an uneasy alliance. Bears and people never completely trust each other, and with good reason. Occasionally a park bear, big, bold, and curious, may become too aggressive for his own good. Sooner or later, he may, like Big Nick and many other bears, face serious trouble because he shares his native woodlands with people who have conditioned him to expect handouts.

—George Laycock

BIG NICK

The Story of a Remarkable Black Bear

Chapter
1

With winter's first snow the old she-bear sensed that the time of her long sleep was approaching. She had eaten during recent weeks until it seemed she could hold no more. Energy was stored in the layers of soft fat beneath her thick coat of black fur. Now she must find a place to spend the winter and give birth to her young.

She pushed her sharp nose through the tangled laurel thicket and wedged her massive body deeper and deeper into the underbrush. Her shoulders forced their own tunnel beneath the low limbs, and as she passed the tunnel closed behind her.

Deep in the undergrowth now, she walked on broad padded feet along the foot of a cliff. Eventually she came upon a hole in the rock face and stuck her nose in to investigate. Two beady eyes stared out at her. Some creature at the back of the little cave bared white fangs and hissed as the black form of the bear shut out most of the light of this late autumn day.

The old bear did not withdraw in surprise, and for that matter did not withdraw at all. With steel-trap speed, she struck out one giant front foot and felt her claws puncture the soft fur of the creature.

She peeled back the coarse fur of the opossum and ate in the semidarkness of the cave. Then she picked up the tattered remnants and moved to the light at the front of the cave. There she lay down and stretched out with her front paws extended before her, the 'possum carcass resting between them. Finally, with an angry swat of one front paw she swept the remnants from her. Now she stretched and looked around; her world seemed in order. There were no strange odors on the early winter winds and no threatening sounds came to her sharp ears. Her limited eyesight detected nothing in the nearby brush to frighten her. Without rising again, she curled up on the leaves at the entrance of the cave and shortly she was sleeping—a great, furry, round ball.

Hours later she awakened abruptly and lifted her head to listen to the baying of a pack of hounds far down the mountainside. The depth of the virgin woodlands helped muffle the hated sounds, but the old she-bear knew where the hounds were. For a short time she lay there fully alert. It seemed that she might get up from this hidden and protected place and go toward the top of the mountain, away from the hounds.

But even as she listened, the barking of the dogs

grew faint. With the dying sounds her calm returned. Rested now, she stood up. For long moments she seemed undetermined as to what she should do. She felt a slight urge to eat and, wandering a short distance, consumed some berries from a mountain ash tree. Then she turned back restlessly to her place beneath the rock. She sniffed carefully around the interior. It was not a deep cave, but a shallow one, only slightly larger than the female bear.

She scratched at the loose earth in the floor of the cave until she had hollowed out a depression there. Then she wandered outside and searched the nearby thicket for materials with which to line her bed. For several hours she brought back weeds and ferns, a few at a time, to make a thin blanket between the dusty earth and her great soft body. For a long time she sat in the middle of her nest, a black bear in the black shadows, the tops of her pointed ears almost touching the rough stone above her. Finally she lay down and curled up to sleep.

All through the days and nights that followed she sank deeper and deeper into the stupor of her winter sleep. Her sensitive ears were closed against the sounds of winter, the wind in the bare limbs of the hardwoods, the plaintive little songs of the chickadees and titmice.

But her sleep was not the true hibernation of the woodchuck. If a disturbance were great enough, she might rise sluggishly from her bed and move reluctantly to a new area. In winter, however, when she slept, it was possible for humans or hounds who moved quietly through the woodlands to come upon her before she knew of their presence; they might destroy her before she realized her danger.

Gradually the rate of her heartbeat slowed, and most of her bodily functions slowed down or ceased. From its summertime level of 98.6 degrees Fahrenheit her body temperature dropped to 93 degrees. The four-inch layer of fat built up beneath her fur would supply her body with energy and, later, provide milk for her young.

As she slept, the old she-bear sometimes wheezed and snored, and frequently shivered in the cold. For long hours, and sometimes for days, she seemed not to move a muscle. But in the middle of a dark moonless night in late January she stirred uneasily in her bed. Changes within her body slowly awakened her. For some time she lay in this sluggish dream world, halfway between sleep and reality. Later that night her three cubs were born. Seven and a half months had passed since the week in June when she had mated.

The experience of giving birth was not new to the old she-bear. Two winters earlier she had given birth to twin cubs, and two winters before that to another set of twins. In the years she had borne young, she had added a total of thirteen cubs to the bear population of the Great Smoky Mountains.

For an animal as large as she was, her babies were indeed small. Each of them was scarcely as long as one of its mother's footprints. They weighed only half a pound each, half as much as an adult gray squirrel. If the female had been fully awake in the hours that followed, she would have seen in the dim light of the chilled cave that her helpless young were almost naked, and that their eyes and ears were closed.

Almost from the beginning there were noticeable differences among the triplets. One was longer and a few ounces heavier than either his brother or sister. In the following days he fed more vigorously and more often on his mother's milk. By the time he was twenty-five days old, the cub had put on a brownish fur coat, so flimsy that for warmth he must still snuggle close to his mother's body.

By his fortieth day there were brief moments when he saw shapes and forms in the dull light. Then there were long periods when it was as black as ever. But his world was small and his needs were few.

By the time he was two months old the cub weighed ten times as much as he had on the day of his birth.

Even before his mother came out of her winter sleep, the cub was frequently wide awake and active for short periods. One warming afternoon he rose on his skinny, wobbly legs and wandered a few steps from his mother's side. The glowing brilliance of the light outside drew him. He moved toward it. At the entrance of the cave he stood, unable to comprehend the wondrous and fearful new world spread before him.

One step at a time he went, until the warmth of the sun settled on his black fur. He stood fully exposed beside the hole in the rocks.

Fifty feet above the entrance to the cave a gaunt yellow bobcat noted the movement of the cub. The cat froze in position, his glinting eyes on the little bear. The bobcat knew that the old she-bear must be somewhere nearby, but there was no sight of the older bear now. The lean sides of the tawny cat testified to his hunger. One pace at a time he crept toward the cub. He was closing the distance, putting himself into position for a final leap.

Suddenly, at the last moment, the cat settled back into a crouching position. He had changed his mind. There, between him and his intended meal, the old female had appeared like a black wall risen out of the earth. While the cat watched, the old bear picked up her cub by the head and carried him back to safety. In her foggy, sleep-ridden mind she had not even sensed the presence of the cat. She had awakened to the disturbing knowledge that one of her cubs was away from her side, and she had gone to bring him back.

For two more days the female and her cubs stayed on in the place of the winter sleep. Then one day when the snow blanket was melting and running down the steep slopes in rivulets and streams, the female took her cubs out on the mountainside and into her world of free-roaming black bears.

Chapter

2

The winter den where her three cubs were born lay near the center of the old female's territory and a quarter of a mile inside the boundary of the big national park. Beyond the border of the park lay the irregularly shaped holdings of Herb Gordon, who looked upon all bears, and most people, as enemies.

Half a mile farther along the cove lay the Swopes' farm. There were three Swopes, if you didn't count hound dogs. Luther Swope's ancestors had taken their living from the hills for many generations, and in spite of the fact that many their age had gone to live in northern cities, Luther, his wife, and his son Johnny remained. To nine-year-old John, the mountains were filled with exciting adventures.

In and out of the national park the old female bear wandered freely, over both of these farms and others as

11

well. But few farmers ever saw her, and in this fact her safety lay.

One day late in May the old female traveled along the border of the park and came to the woods at the back of the Gordon farm. Her small cubs sometimes ran at her heels but often walked, almost hidden, beneath her belly. She veered to the west and left the safety of the park behind.

She stopped once to tear apart a rotting log, from which she extracted three fat white grubs. Then she discovered a nest of ants, and with a swipe of her paw tore into the top. She placed her flat paw on the ant nest and held it there until ants in great numbers scurried over the furry invader. Then she licked the ants from her paw and placed it once more back on the ant nest for a second helping.

The cubs stopped their wrestling and watched this curious episode. The largest cub touched the ant nest with his nose. The ants crawling onto his nose made a strange tickling sensation, and the cub drew his head back sharply. Then he grew alarmed at the strangeness of the experience. He rubbed his nose in the leaves, first to one side then the other, and swatted at his face with his tiny paws. He jumped stiff-legged into the air and, as he fell, rolled over and over until eventually he dislodged the last of the tiny strange creatures.

Later, while the old female explored along the edge of a great rotting log, the largest of her three cubs wandered a few feet away and quickly put the log between himself and his mother. Like his mother, he scratched at the edge of the log.

Suddenly, from beneath the leaves, some unseen creature seemed to jump up and bite so hard into the toes of his right front foot that he cried out in surprise and pain.

Whatever it was still clung to him. In his panic the cub tumbled over in the leaves. He tried to scramble back to his mother's side, but some strange force jolted him to a sudden stop. Flashes of searing pain shot through his foot and leg. With each movement it grew worse. Filled now with fear of the unknown, he squawled again and again.

At the first outcry from her cub the female snorted and ran around the log, prepared for battle. But there was nothing to attack. There was no creature menacing him. This frustrated the old bear. She growled at the cub.

Crouched down in the leaves, the cub whimpered constantly. Then the old female sniffed at the trapped foot and saw for the first time the object that held him, the steel trap Gordon had forgotten and left through the seasons, waiting in vain for a raccoon that never came. Long years of experience around the farms and the national park had taught the she-bear to associate metal with people. But she found no man odor on this device; it had long since disappeared. She growled anyway, in

13

her anger. She reached out and touched the chain with her paw, but this put such painful pressure on the cub's foot that he cried out again, and his mother withdrew her foot.

Here was a situation beyond her understanding. She knew how to knock a lid from a garbage can, tear apart a bee hive to get at the honey, and swat a picnic basket apart with a single blow of her paw. She knew how to eat fish from a metal stringer without getting injured and how to open tin cans without a can opener, but nowhere had she gained the knowledge that would help her remove her cub from a steel trap.

Eventually she lay down close beside the cub as if to comfort him; his whimpering ceased. He pushed close to the great warm body of his mother. Numbness had dulled the pain in his foot, and by lying quite still he seemed almost to forget that he was trapped. His eyes closed and he slept.

Soon, as if she had forgotten the plight of her cub, the old female stood up and walked slowly away. The two smaller cubs moved to her and walked beside her. She had gone but a few yards when the larger cub awakened. He stumbled to stand up and again felt the flashing pains through his mutilated foot. He cried out to his mother in alarm, although he remembered now not to jerk on the chain.

She wheeled and returned to his side as he crouched in the leaves, but withheld the cuffing that might otherwise have greeted a cub who disobeyed her commands.

She sensed that punishment would not solve her problem. During the remainder of that night she did not try to leave. She had attempted this once and had discovered the cub could not follow. The bears lay there through the rest of the night drawing comfort from each other's presence, each aware that some danger confronted them. The old female did not sleep, for this place disturbed her. It lacked the dense cover into which she usually took her cubs to bed down. The woods in all directions were open to her view as the first light of the new day brought objects into focus. Nearby, a wood thrush offered a morning song and the shadowy form of a great horned owl passed through the branches above, but the bear paid neither any attention.

A few hours later on this brilliant spring morning Johnny Swope took his father's three hounds and headed for the forest. Down the narrow path, past the barn, and through the pasture field at the end of the cove the boy and the hounds raced for the sheer joy of running. This was the season of awakening. Around the Swope farm and up the mountains beyond, spring advanced toward the high ridges and the balds and left in its wake the pastel greens of new foliage and the brilliant colors of spring flowers.

In the Smokies, spring comes first to the valleys. Week by week it advances up the slopes. It comes early to the elevations of two thousand feet such as the cove where the Swopes lived. Then spring creeps on up to three thousand feet, and finally four thousand, where the

15

eastern hemlocks flourish. It is at these elevations, in the protected timberlands inside the national park, that the hemlocks still stand in virgin splendor, untouched by axes and saws. And here among them is a belt of northern hardwoods of record proportions—great sugar maples, yellow buckeye trees, yellow birch, and the beech with its spreading gray limbs.

At four thousand feet the spruce and fir have begun to mix with the spectacular hardwoods, and in the high reaches the climate and vegetation become much like those far north in Canada. There are spruce and fir forests and northern birds to match these nothern trees. In the spruce-fir woodlands are the red-breasted nuthatches, juncos, golden-crowned kinglets, saw-whet owls, brown creepers, and even the raven, the great, shy black symbol of vast wilderness solitude.

These mountains were Johnny Swope's world. Trails of game and people crisscrossed them. And the trails became familiar woodland avenues for boys and dogs free to roam the hills and hollows.

Down one slope, across the creek, and up the mountain he followed the trail. Then he heard the hounds baying farther up the mountain ahead of him.

The three hounds came upon the family of bears suddenly. The dark bulk of the old bear rose before them. They had not sensed her presence. She issued a low growl as the dogs slid to a halt and began barking and yapping in great commotion.

The preceding twenty-four hours had filled the old

16

female with frustrating rage. Her short temper had grown shorter with every passing hour. By morning she was ready to rip open any foreign creature within reach of her long slashing claws.

She rushed upon the dogs but the agile hounds escaped the cutting claws and drew back to encircle and harass her. With her usual command the old bear ordered the two free cubs to climb to safety, and they scooted up a nearby oak tree to sit and stare down in wonder. Then the old bear bolted into the depths of the forest, finding in the action sudden release for her pent-up anger.

Johnny saw the two treed cubs almost at once, and then a slight motion in the leaves beside the log attracted his attention. He bent over the trapped cub to see what kept him in this place, and discovered the aging steel trap, brown with rust, secured to the log by three feet of chain. He must free this trapped cub while the old bear was away with the dogs, and he must do it quickly. "Little one," he thought, "maybe no heavier than a crock of milk. Why, I could carry him easy."

Chapter
3

*N*ow *the cub saw the boy remove his blue denim* jacket. Then it came down quickly over him and shut out the light. Inside the darkness of the jacket the bear jerked and heaved against the forces that restrained him. For a moment the fearful trap on his foot was forgotten. The coat and the boy were now his biggest threat.

The cub rolled and tried to scratch the cloth away from his face, but it was held down tighter than ever. Gradually the bear sensed that his struggle was accomplishing nothing. The trapped foot now hurt worse. The cub bawled and whimpered, his pain compounded with panic.

He sensed next that the creature who had caught him was reaching inside the jacket. A new fear choked him. He attempted to scratch and claw at the hand, but his legs were restrained so tightly that he could not reach it. Tighter and tighter the cub felt his body forced against the ground. There was no longer hope—he was at the mercy of this large creature.

But the hand was not trying to hurt him. At first it rested firmly on his back. Then it slid down the silky fur of his side until it touched his shoulder. Now it moved more cautiously than ever. Then the creature was working, not with the bear, but with the steel that gripped his damaged foot. There was a pressure on the trap and this sent new spasms of pain shooting through the lacerated paw. Then suddenly the steel that had held his foot for so many hours relaxed its grip. The trap jaws were held open and his paw carefully pulled away from the steel.

The cub felt himself being lifted up. The firm earth was no longer beneath him and this frightened him once more, especially since the covering still enveloped him. He kicked and struggled inside the jacket but the harder he struggled, the tighter the boy gripped him. Now the boy was running, and the cub was jolted up and down. He whimpered and cried out as the boy ran down the long, timbered slope of the mountain. Here and there Johnny forced his path through thick-growing underbrush, but usually he stayed on the game and livestock trails that led back to his father's barn. Eventually the cub stopped struggling and forced the end of his nose into the space between the boy's body and his arm, and pulled up the injured foot to relieve the pressure against it.

Far up the mountain the old female took refuge in a tree, where she was half an hour later when two park

19

workers came down the trail. They chased the dogs from the vicinity and eventually she descended the tree and bolted off. A great uneasiness swept over her. She raced back to where she had left her cubs, one in a trap beside a great log, the other two clinging to the side of a tree.

She came to the tree where her cubs were and grunted. One of them came scooting quickly to the ground working his way around and around the tree trunk as he descended. The other cub, however, did not obey. The female grunted one more time and looked up in his direction. She was in no mood to accept disobedience. She grunted a third time and eventually the cub, in spite of the strange and frightening events he had witnessed on the ground below, came uneasily down the tree. His mother promptly waddled up to him and with one broad paw reached out and cuffed him severely on his head. He rolled over and over through the leaves, crying out in pained surprise. When he scrambled to his feet, he trotted obediently back to his mother.

With her two small cubs walking close to her, the female now returned to the log where she had left her third cub. Through the puzzling day and night she had come to know every feature of the landscape around this rotting log. But now she was confused, and suddenly apprehensive. The third cub was not there. She sniffed the base of the log where the cub had lain. The trap was still there. The blood of her cub marked it. The smell of her cub was there, but so was the smell of man. The old female had known this odor for many years, and many times when she had found the man odor strong, she had discovered unexpected trouble. She growled now from the depths of her throat. She walked all around the log and sniffed the ground carefully as she padded along. Then she came to the place where the boy had left his trail both coming and going. And his scent was strong in her nostrils.

Somehow she associated the disappearance of her helpless cub with the trail of the human. The familiar odor of her cub clung to each branch and leaf it had touched. Her native caution deserted her. Her fear of man was suddenly overcome by her concern for her young. She began running at full speed along the trail the boy had left.

She had covered no more than a hundred feet when the whimpering of her cubs, stumbling behind to keep within sight of her, suddenly brought her attention back to the young that had not been lost. She turned on the cubs and, with the explosive woof they had come to understand, sent them up the large trunk of a wild cherry tree to await her return.

She covered the downhill mile to Spicer Creek much faster than the boy had run it. Like a black demon she rustled through the forest with the wind making tears run down her jaws. She stopped only when she needed to check the trail. In one place particularly she could sense the odor of her cub. There was a small rock here where the boy had sat only long enough to readjust the slipping bulk of the cub beneath his jacket, and the odor of cub lingered around the place with that of its captor.

Suddenly at the edge of the creek she splashed full force into the shallow stream and wallowed to the far side. Then she halted. Somewhere she had lost the trail. She could no longer smell of the boy or the cub. She stopped long enough to listen carefully, but there came to her ears only the familiar bird calls and, far off in the park, the noise of automobiles grinding up a mountain highway. Five minutes earlier she might have heard the running feet of a boy far up the mountain across the valley in the direction of the Swope place, but now there was nothing.

She walked up the side of the creek a short distance and still did not find the trail she sought. She turned and walked down and found no trace here either. She recrossed the creek, delighting for the moment in the splashing coolness of the water. But on this side, as well as the other, there was no longer any trace of the cub or the boy who had taken him. The old female remembered the two cubs in the cherry tree and slowly, grunting in her frustration and confusion, she began plodding up the mountainside alone.

Chapter 4

At the edge of the clearing John stopped. He now remembered his father's dogs, the three lean, long-legged hounds conditioned by generations of ancestry to attack and kill bears. But the hounds were still somewhere in the forest. Here in the yard and around the barn there was no one to see him, no dog to bark a warning. He skirted around the edge of the woods, placing the barn between himself and the house. He paused to catch his breath, then dashed across the little pasture to the safety of the barn. He ran to the big door and slipped through it out of the sunlight into the cool semi-darkness inside. Then he paused and leaned against the wall to think. Where could a person hide a bear?

He felt a twinge of guilt. He would quickly have taken an easier problem to his father. But what would his father say if he suddenly asked, "Reckon it's all right if I keep a bear?" John was afraid of the answer, and now he already had the bear and wanted to keep it as much as he had ever wanted anything.

To the Swopes, as to all families in these hills, the bears were a part of living, a part of the mountains. John had heard talk of bears and bear hunts all his life. He had heard how his great-grandparents rendered down each fall, the thick fat layer from a bear, which provided a winter's supply of pure, white, odorless lard for the families in these hills. But he had heard mostly the tales of destruction caused by bears and the stories of bravery of hunters who pursued them.

His own great-grandfather, William Swope, whom he had never seen, must have been the bravest of all the bear hunters. Not many mountain boys could say—and believe it—that their great-grandfather had killed a bear single-handed with nothing but a knife.

Uncounted times he had heard his father tell the story of the standers who took their places on the ridges waiting for the bears to cross and the hunters who went with the dogs to chase the bears from their beds.

The laurel slicks grew so dense and tangled a man could not get through without crawling, but the men sent their dogs in to fight the bears. On the second day of that famous hunt Grandpa Swope got a chance to win a bet he had made.

He stood waiting on the uphill side of the thicket, and suddenly the dogs began raising an unearthly commotion. Then within plain sight, the bear and all the hounds came tumbling and snarling out of the brush.

25

The bear ran off with the yelling hounds close on his heels, and the man ran as fast as he could behind them. The bear came to the face of a rock ledge and there he took his stand. In his fury he turned on the hounds and rose to his hind feet to fight with his sharp front claws.

The man was edging in closer all the time, his hunting knife gripped tightly in his hand. Then one of the hounds attacked the bear from the far side and the bear dropped to all four feet and turned to take care of this new threat. As the creature turned from him, the man lunged forward. He reached over and plunged his knife hilt-deep into the chest cavity of the animal.

With a yell of rage the bear clawed at the place the knife had entered. This was always a major point of the story. By attacking the bear on the off-side, the man allowed himself that vital instant in which to leap back and make good his own escape. John's father always ended the story the same way: "By the time the bear knew where Grandpa was, Grandpa wasn't nowhere abouts. And when the other men came up the mountain they found the dogs yapping all around, and grandpa sitting on the dead bear wipin' his knife blade on the fur."

Johnny looked around the inside of the barn. His father came here many times each day. But attached to the back of the barn was a small lean-to built long ago and used only a few weeks each fall as a tobacco-stripping shed.

There were two doors to the shed, one from inside

the barn and another from outdoors. John forced the
creaking door open and entered the shed from the barn.
He closed the door behind him and hooked it, and then
looked around at the tiny room.

There was a workbench along one wall where tobacco leaves had once been stripped from the tough
brown stalks and tied into "hands" to cure. There was
nothing else in the room. The single window was
boarded up, and John stood staring around him for a full
minute before his vision adjusted to the darkness.

He eased himself to the floor with the bear in his lap
and then, slowly and gently, uncovered the cub. Unlike
his lumbering mother, the cub until this day had had no
experience, either good or bad, with people. But he
sensed that this strange creature putting its hands on his
furry coat was not to be trusted. Fear of the unfamiliar
gripped the cub and in his effort to bolt from the boy's
lap he tumbled clumsily onto his back on the dusty floor.
He scrambled around trying to right himself, and no
sooner did he get his feet beneath him again than his
captor grabbed him. The cub struggled against the boy.
Johnny chuckled, "You're full of the Old Nick, aren't
you, boy?"

Again the cub felt the stabbing pain of his injured
foot. He stood on three legs and held the other foot off
the floor as he tried to back farther from Johnny into a
dark corner of the shed. He heard sounds from the
human.

"That foot hurts you plenty, doesn't it, boy?" John

said quietly. "You better let me put something on it for you." For the first time he was getting a really good look at the cub—his cub.

He reached out once more to touch the soft fur. With his uninjured paw the cub made a fast jab at John's extended fingers. The action put the cub's weight on his injured paw and again he tumbled to the floor, unable to support himself. Quickly, however, he righted himself and backed farther into the corner and sat there glaring at the boy. The cub showed no quaking fear. He watched every movement the boy made, and snorted once or twice in what seemed to John to be open defiance. "Say, you really got the Old Nick in you," John said. "Nobody going to get the best of you. And smartness goes with spirit. I think I found me the right cub, sure enough, and the right name for you too. We're gonna have to understand each other sooner or later, Nick. First thing I gotta do is fix up that paw."

Johnny stepped out of the stripping shed as quietly as a shadow, leaving the little bear crouched in the dark corner beneath the bench. Inside the corn crib he found two torn burlap grain sacks, and he took these back to the shed. "Here's a couple of gunny sacks for a bed," he said to the cub. He pushed the burlap bags down beside the bear and shortly the whimpering cub lay down on them. Long hours had passed since he had awakened beside the log. Even the hunger inside him and the fear of the boy's nearness could no longer keep him awake. He closed his eyes and he slept.

Very quietly, John rose to his feet and backed softly from the shed. He closed the door as gently as he could. "If I take it easy with him," he thought, "and don't make quick motions, he won't likely get so scared. And maybe when he finds out that I'm his friend we'll get along. He's got spunk all right."

His mother was busy in the bedroom "reddin' up" when John returned to the house. He found a piece of old cloth in the kitchen closet. He took the antiseptic salve from the shelf and forced it into the pocket of his pants. Then with a quick glance in his mother's direction, he went to the table and spread a piece of bread with butter and jelly. "You hungry already?" His mother was standing in the bedroom door.

"Just getting a piece of bread, Mom," he said. "Okay?"

His mother smiled. "Sure it is, honey. If you're hungry, you're hungry."

John, trying not to hurry, took a small bite from the slice of bread as he went out the kitchen door. He ran through the flock of calico-colored chickens in the yard, and pushed the creaking shed door open slowly. As his eyes adjusted to the darkness again, he could see the cub still sleeping in the corner. He moved to the cub and opened the can of salve he had taken from his pocket. He touched the bear's fur and the little animal moved beneath his hands. But as the boy began to spread salve on the stump from which the two toes had been severed, the cub jerked awake.

The boy was leaning over him. Here again was a situation strange to the cub. He wanted to hide beneath his mother, but his mother was not there. He wanted to escape from this creature, but there was no escape. He scooted back into the corner as far and as fast as he could, and his small black eyes stared straight at the boy, challenging him.

Now the boy was holding something in front of his mouth. Nick sniffed the fruit odors of the jelly. His stomach growled, and saliva ran from the soft corners of his mouth. His tongue came out, and he licked the jelly, but because it was the first food a man had offered him and because he was not yet accustomed to human food, he refused to eat the bread. When the jelly was all gone he licked his lips with his red curling tongue and sat down again on the burlap bags. He refused to eat any more.

"Young bears," John was thinking, "need milk, just like young pigs or calves or babies." Then he recalled the bottle and nipple his mother had used the year before to feed the three pigs orphaned when the old sow took sick and died. He found the bottle on a shelf behind the stall where they milked Queenie every morning and evening. He cleaned the bottle at the horse trough. Now he needed milk, but he needed warm milk. Queenie was his answer. He found an empty coffee can to take with him to the pasture behind the barn. He managed to herd the docile cow into a corner of the pasture. She stood there patient and uncomprehending while John squatted by her right side and filled the can with warm milk.

30

"Thanks, Queenie," he said, and walked quickly back to the barn.

Nick soon learned to take milk from a bottle. He drank greedily until John was afraid he would get too much at once and withdrew the milk. Then he left the cub alone to become accustomed to his new home.

During the cub's first evening in the stripping shed the loneliness and strangeness of his surroundings filled him with distress. But no matter how much he whimpered, his mother did not come to him. Her great,

shaggy, warm body was not there to cover him or to hide him from the rest of the world.

Darkness had settled over the mountains and sent the Swopes indoors for the night. Heavy storm clouds pushed in like black blankets over the hills. Lightning flashed from cloud to cloud and slashed at the mountainsides.

Then the rain came, a conquering force marching across the mountains. It beat out a kettle-drum roll on the old tin roof. Here again was a frightening new sound to the cub.

Other storms in recent weeks had taught the little bear something of the cold wetness and the awesome power of weather in the mountains. But always there had been his mother. At the coming of rain she would permit her cubs to hide beneath her shaggy coat. Gone now was the warm, furry comfort. He felt alone and exposed to the forces of the rumbling sounds, the strange pounding noise above him, and the light that flashed repeatedly through the cracks of his shed. Throughout the storm he sat on the burlap bags pushing himself far back beneath the work table, his eyes wide. He looked nervously about him at each brief flash of lightning. All the time he whimpered, but his mother did not come.

Up in the house Johnny Swope lay wide awake in his iron bed. Ordinarily he slept with the soundness of the very young. If his father rose to look after the stock in the night, John seldom knew it until breakfast time. But this night was different. From the time he went to bed until the storm began, he did not sleep.

As soon as his parents had gone to bed, John dressed, pulled on a heavy jacket, and quietly let himself out into the storm. His bare feet splashed across the yard to the barn. Nick still crouched in the corner where John had left him. Now the warmth of the boy's body was welcome. So was the bottle of milk he brought. Soon the boy slept curled up in the corner of the shed with the cub snugly asleep against him.

Toward morning John awoke. He wondered at first where he was. Then he remembered. He put his hand on the cub. The bear slept on. John heard a rooster crow. Soon his father and mother would be out of bed and moving around the house; time was short. He eased himself away from the sleeping cub and ran back through the yard in the first light of dawn. Then he was in his own bed again, and except for his damp clothes dropped on the floor beside him, he might have been there all night. He slept again.

Late the following afternoon strange footsteps awakened Nick. Uneasiness swept over the tiny bear. He had learned quickly to accept the visits of the boy. He connected them with warm milk and sweet food. A bond was already forming between the boy and the cub.

But now it was a stranger who opened the door. The voice was strange too. "Well I'll be . . ." said Luther Swope. He leaned over the cub and Nick drew back into his corner and swatted at the big hand reaching out to him.

At this moment Johnny came into the barn. He saw at once that the door to the stripping shed stood ajar. He ran to shut the door before the cub could escape. Then his father stepped out.

"A bear's a pretty hard thing to hide," Luther said. John stood staring down at his bare feet.

Luther listened carefully as the boy related the details of the cub's capture. "Lucky the old she-bear didn't catch you and tear you up!" he said. "They don't put up with man nor beast fooling with their cubs. I always told you that."

"But when I grabbed Nick up," John answered, "the old she-bear was runnin' off from Blue and Limp and Lead, and it looked like I had plenty of time. Then, to keep her from trackin' me home I walked up the creek 'most a mile."

The silence grew between Luther and his son. "I should have asked," John said quietly. He was still staring at his bare feet.

"That's right," his father said. "We should have talked it over, like men, then come to a right decision."

Suddenly standing there before his father John knew what he had not let himself think during the brief time that he had possessed the pet cub: there really was no chance of keeping the bear on the farm. Suddenly he wished he had released the cub from the trap and just left him beside the great log in the deep woods. He spoke very slowly and haltingly. "I reckon I better figure out something to do with him."

"I reckon we better," his father added quietly, "and the sooner the better."

Chapter
5

For two days the bear and her remaining cubs stayed within a quarter of a mile of the crossing where the boy's trail had ended. Wild creatures may know anger when their young are threatened, but what is done is soon forgotten. Periods of mourning for individuals lost are brief indeed. The old bear now turned her full attention to the needs of her remaining cubs.

She dug fat white grubs from rotting logs and brought up appetizing roots from the leaf litter of the forest floor. She came once upon the nest of a ruffed grouse. The brown hen bird launched herself from her leafy nest at the base of a maple tree inches ahead of the she-bear's nose and, with a noise like that of a distant chain saw, plummeted in an irregular course through the woods. Behind her, the old bear ate every one of her twelve pale brown eggs.

Three days after the loss of her cub, the old female led her other two cubs beyond the boundaries of the park and down the mountainside. Early that evening they moved beyond Herb Gordon's farm and came eventually to the edge of the clearing behind Swope's barnyard.

There was that night a first-quarter moon, and the air was soft with the coming of summer. The singing tree toads had the shrill music of the crickets for background. The whippoorwill's melancholy call came endlessly from the timbered slopes. The song never changed, but if it meant something to these birds of the night it was hardly worthy of note to the wandering black bear.

Gradually, dim memories had come to life in her head. The outlines of these buildings were vaguely familiar. In other years, with other cubs, she had come to this place. And she knew now why her memories guided her steps.

She walked in her plodding fashion from the edge of the timber and into the moonlit pasture. The shaggy form of the old black female moved now toward the barn.

At the edge of the other pasture beyond his barn, Luther Swope kept five hives of bees.

Since the time when the earliest domestic bees had been carried to these hills by the white settlers, marauding bears had shared the honey with the mountain people. The closer she came to the Swope buildings the stronger the memory of the honey became. She hurried in her eagerness until the cubs found it increasingly difficult to keep up the pace.

The path the old bear had set for herself would take her close to the Swope barn. The wind blew from the direction of the house out over the barnyard, and the hounds chained close to the house slept on as she moved quietly on her padded feet.

Around the edge of the barn came the shadowy forms of the bears. Here the female found her path blocked by the stripping shed that jutted out before her. She veered to the right to walk around the shed, but as she did so, she stopped short. For a brief moment she stood confused by the mixture of smells in this place where men lived. She had picked up the odor of her cub mingled with the man odors, and angry memories flooded through her mind. Asleep now on the burlap bags, her lost cub lay only a few feet away beyond the wooden wall.

The old female stood moving her head from side to side. The log. The trap. The man odor. The man odor was strong in this place, the same man odor she had known in the woods at the time her cub disappeared. She rose to the full height of her great body and angrily cut long, raking claw marks into the side of the shed.

At the sound the hounds up by the house set up a racket. Luther Swope awakened and mumbled, "What in tarnation's bothering them hounds!" But the wind was with the bears. The dogs grew quiet again except for an occasional yelp, and did nothing further to announce the bear's presence.

The old female sniffed all around the base of the shed. She searched for a way in which to dispose of this barrier between her and her cub. Inside, the cub was wide awake. The nearness of his mother excited him. Here was the creature he had first known in the world— his first food, his first warmth, his earliest protection. The big bear was so close Nick could hear her breathing. The cub whimpered and rose from his bed. He limped along the edge of the weathered wooden wall that stood as a barrier between them. He stood on his rear feet and scratched as high as he could on the boards. He pushed his little nose into the crack between two boards and then he clawed at it as an older and more experienced bear might have done.

When the old female was unable to tear down the solid wall, she moved to a new place and tried again. She stood up and tore at the top of the boards. Then she dropped to all fours and walked along the base of the wall until she came to the side of the shed where the top of the ill-fitting door left a large crack.

Here, by standing on her hind feet, the female could easily reach the top of the door. She hooked her claws behind the boards, and with the full strength of her massive shoulders and forearms ripped the door apart board by board, as if finding in the destruction itself some fulfillment of a primitive, driving urge until the door lay in pieces on the ground. She walked deliberately into the

shed, where Nick stood in the dark corner. For a few
minutes she nuzzled him, licked his fur, and made soft
sounds, while he nursed. Then she turned and left the
shed. Close at her heels came Nick, free again to roam
the secluded, hidden recesses of the mountains.

At the sound of the splintering door the hounds had
once more set up their racket. Luther came to the door
of the farmhouse, but he came too late. He listened, but

heard nothing except his dogs. He peered into the night and saw nothing to arouse his curiosity. "Barkin' at the moon again," he decided. He yelled at the dogs to stop their racket, and went back to bed, undisturbed this time until the first light of morning came.

Across the open pasture the old female, trailed by her cubs, quickly closed the distance between the barn and the woods from which she had emerged a short time before.

She had forgotten the lure of the honey. The barking of the Swope hounds had filled the old female with renewed caution and fear for the welfare of her cubs. This night had been filled with strange events. She was uneasy and nervous. She made haste away from the farms in the hollow. Down the hill her trail led once more to the creek. With her clumsy cubs splashing gaily behind her, the old female crossed the creek at almost the same spot John had carried Nick out of the water three days earlier.

An hour later at dawn, her route carried her and her cubs to the boundary of the national park and into the depths of its sanctuary.

Chapter

6

These warm days of their first spring were filled with wonder for the tiny cubs. The old female, walking slowly so that her cubs could keep up with her, traveled in a leisurely way through her woodland territory. She stopped frequently and seldom refused to sit and let the cubs nurse when they were hungry. As they took her rich, satisfying milk they emitted high humming noises that sounded like the buzzing of insects. And once they were fed the cubs were ready to curl up and sleep against the broad, warm side of their mother.

At this age they weighed ten times their weight at birth, but even this gain brought them only to the six- or eight-pound class. They were awkward little roly-poly black creatures with long brown noses, stiff erect ears, and gleaming little eyes that searched through each waking hour for any mischief in which cub bears might engage.

Nick was the largest of the three cubs and almost everything attracted his attention. If a leaf blew past he might decide to give chase. Then the other two cubs would race him for the prize. Eventually all three would come together in a furry mass, rolling over and over in a fast-paced game of pushing, tugging, sparring, and trying to get on top of each other.

Frequently the old female would play these games with them. Lying on her side or back she would permit the cubs to clamber over her great soft body. When she tired of the game, she stood up to wander away in search of food or a more protected spot in which to seclude her cubs. Sometimes as her three cubs played their endless games she sat looking at them as though she took deep and satisfying pride in the sight of them and the obvious joy they took in living during these carefree days.

Play and lessons blended together as the old female introduced her young to new elements in their environment. Gradually her cubs would learn from her that bears find food in a great variety of plants and animals. She taught them to dig for roots and that the earthworms uncovered in the search were not to be wasted. Bits of leaves and grass and the delicate petals of spring flowers, such as the spring beauty and dogtooth violets, were sampled too. She taught her young to search for crayfish by the edges of the creeks. And occasionally they came upon the nest of a small bird on the ground or within reach of the old female, and a tragedy in the life of one forest creature lent strength to the bodies of others.

Through these weeks and on into late summer, when cubs are weaned from their mother's milk, they naturally rely more and more on the wild foods gleaned from the forest.

One day in a pool along a tumbling trout stream the female coaxed her cubs farther and farther from the shore. All at once they realized that their feet no longer touched bottom. The cubs paddled frantically at first, then with growing confidence. As Nick emerged from the stream he turned his head from one side to the other, curiously watching the clear water drip off his smooth coat.

After that he sometimes ran straight to the edge of any creek they approached and jumped wildly into it. Like a flat rock, his body would smack against the surface of the water and send spray up and over him. Then, depending on the depth of the water, he would wade or paddle until his mother made him get out of his swimming pool.

One afternoon the old female headed through the deep forest toward the creek and a frothing little pool below a riffle where the banks of the stream were thickly hidden by mountain laurel and blanketed with moist green moss. They were walking with their peculiar side-swinging gait along a heavily used bear trail when the old female suddenly stopped and lifted her head to listen. Somewhere below them in the depths of the forest was a truck moving slowly along the twisting, narrow service road. Gradually the truck moved farther and farther away, until eventually it could no longer be heard. Now the bears moved on toward the creek below where the truck had been just a short time before.

The cubs ran ahead of their mother and splashed

gleefully into the water. Dozens of panic-stricken eight-inch trout scurried in all directions and churned the surface of the stream in a manner that was quickly noticed by the old female. As good fortune would have it, she had arrived with her family within minutes after the hatchery truck had been there with its tankload of rainbow trout. It is in such secluded places as this that fish managers attempt to stock trout and give them a chance to spread along the stream before the concentrations are discovered. In those early moments before the fish had fully adjusted to the shock of the colder water they were at the mercy of the bears.

The cubs were suddenly surrounded by fish. Nick made a swipe at a nearby group and missed them all. He fell off balance from the force of his blow and tumbled with a splash onto his side. He scrambled to his feet and made another quick jab at one of the trout as he righted himself. He missed this time too, and then, as if to seek advice, he turned to watch what his mother did.

With a lightning-fast movement of her head she caught one of the fish in her teeth and brought it out of the creek and placed it before her cubs. Soon she had the bank shimmering with half a dozen dying trout, and only then did she pause to eat.

The following day the old female took her cubs back to the pool, but the trout had moved out of the crowded waters and only a few remained. The old bear managed to catch one, after much wasted effort. She was still hungry, so she went elsewhere to search for food.

This was the simplicity of her way of living, an un-
planned existence to which her cubs became accustomed.

The days passed quickly, and frequently there were
events new to the cubs. One afternoon the bear family
came upon a wasp nest hanging in the woods. The female
heard the humming and walked from the bear trail
into the woods. She looked up, and there above her hung
the nest, almost as big as one of her cubs.

By standing on her hind legs, the old female reached

47

the limb on which the wasps had built their gray paper globe. She pulled the limb down, and with one swing of her free paw sent the nest crashing to the ground.

She ignored the dozens of angry wasps whirring around her and lighting on her and her cubs. The bears ate the small store of honey and also the white grubs.

The bears lived much of the time in a wet world. Almost daily in these weeks there were rain showers dampening the forests. There were times when the heavy fog caused moisture to collect on the leaves above them and drop to moisten the earth where they walked. Even the clear days revealed the indistinct forms of distant peaks shrouded in a blue haze that seemed always to hover over the mountains and settle into the valleys. But the rains seldom bothered the bears. Frequently the old she-bear would sit or lie down and her cubs would crowd beneath her, protected from the downpour. If the rain persisted, she sometimes took shelter in the recesses of a cliff or under the thick foliage of a rhododendron.

One warm, sunny afternoon she led the cubs through the hardwood timber and down in the direction of the cave in which she had hibernated the winter before. Near the top of a rock cliff the old bear came upon the place where her trail had once led down the cliff to her winter cave, but instead of following this trail she continued along the top of the cliff.

Then the female turned uphill again, toward an abandoned farm clearing where an old log cabin stood, its roof sagging to the ground. As they came into the clearing, the cubs blinked against the great brilliance of the sun, and they saw a strange bear. Because the black stranger had sensed their approach first, he stood high on his rear feet. He was not as large as the old female, and probably not yet fully mature.

The old female growled and rushed at the other bear, who dropped quickly to all four feet and ran to the edge of the woods. But there, as if he didn't know any better, he stopped. The female rushed toward him again, overtaking him this time. With a mighty sweeping blow of her great paw she sent him rolling and squawling among the saplings. He tripped over his feet, stumbling in his haste, and then departed in ignominious retreat. Grumpily, the female turned back and went to her cubs.

Soon the small cubs were wrestling with each other as usual. They sparred and pushed each other, then rolled over and over along the gentle slope toward the edge of the woods.

The old female was feeding on blue violets when her cubs came to the edge of the clearing and followed the path of least resistance downhill into the woods toward the cliff.

At this point the smallest cub came upon a small rusted bucket in the weeds at the edge of the clearing. As cub bears will, the young one sniffed around the open end of the little bucket. Then, to fully explore this strange thing, he stuck his head inside the pail. Now Nick saw his advantage. He hit his smaller brother on the shoulder and waited for him to back out of the bucket and turn on him in revenge. But when his brother lifted his head, the bucket came too. Nick hit his brother again playfully in the side. The only response was a muffled woof from inside the pail.

It was dark in this place. The smaller cub tried backing out as he had from hollow logs, but no matter how far he backed he did not come to the end. Then he tried frantically to throw the strange object from him.

Nick and his sister, puzzled now, sat on their haunches tilting their heads one way then the other to watch this strange game. The bucket and the bear went around and around, and the trapped cub was edging farther and farther downhill.

Above them the old female paused, disturbed by the strangeness of the sounds coming from her playing cubs. She stood up and looked. Then she lowered herself to the ground and trotted toward them. She seldom permitted them to get this far from her.

The female grunted, and the cub whimpered hollowly from within the bucket. At this point he struggled once more to back out, but the bucket would not come off his head and the blinded cub stumbled and fell. He rolled over and over through the leaves, gaining speed with each revolution. Like a rolling cartwheel, he plunged toward the cliff.

The female ran to the edge of the cliff and peered over. She watched her cub fall free through space. Far below he thumped against a great jagged rock, then

50

rolled farther down the forest floor to stop at last by the roots of a tall oak tree. The cub did not move again. The bucket was still stuck to his head with the bail under his chin, leaving tragic evidence of the accident that had occurred.

With her two other cubs trailing close behind her, the old female trotted along the cliff. She began walking stiff-legged toward the bottom of the rock outcropping and reached the place where her cub lay dead. She nosed the cub, and a strange whimper issued from her throat. She sniffed the bucket and growled. She lifted her head and looked around as if seeking some creature to blame. But in the warmth of midday the woods were silent except for the insects.

The bear and her two remaining cubs stayed until the sun went down behind the mountains. The female lay down near her dead cub. Nick and his sister pushed against her deep, shaggy fur. Some time later, they all rose and walked off into the woods without once looking back.

Chapter
7

One *afternoon* *in* *July* *Nick,* *curled* *up* *against* *his* sister, awakened from a deep slumber. He yawned and stretched and sat up in his warm, leafy bed. He looked briefly around him at his limited world and saw the heavy form of his mother sleeping a few yards away in the same thicket. Nick quickly became bored with the inactivity. He reached out one paw and tentatively pushed against the shoulder of his sleeping sister. The other cub grunted, stretched, and went back to sleep. Nick backed three feet away from the small cub and then, as if hurtled from a cannon, he lunged at his sister and hit her squarely in the side. The smaller cub gave an explosive woof and bounded up, ready instantly to meet whatever hazard confronted her. She rushed Nick, and together they rolled over and over in the leaves until they came to the side of their sleeping mother.

When the old bear grunted at her cubs, they paid

no attention. This behavior was, to the old female, completely unacceptable. With a lightning-fast jab of her paw she reached out and swatted the nearest cub, which happened to be Nick. She hit him on the shoulder and sent him rolling into the underbrush. Both cubs, sobered by this sudden rebuke, sat in the leaves looking pleadingly at their mother as if to ask what they had done to merit such treatment. Awakened now, the old she-bear sat up and yawned. She stood up and as she padded along began in a leisurely way to turn over rocks and tear apart such small logs as she could find. Her cubs followed closely behind her, pausing occasionally in their wanderings to take exploratory slaps at each other. Sometimes they stood up on their hind feet and sparred like midget fur-coated boxers.

Suddenly the old bear grunted at the cubs, giving them her command for silence. She stood to her full height, pushing aside the branches above her as she did so. From this position she listened quietly for a few moments. There was no mistaking the sound. Somewhere below, far down in the valley, the hounds were running. The old she-bear dropped to all four feet and stood motionless, still listening. She determined that the hounds were on a trail up the mountainside in the direction of the refuge where she and her cubs had known peace and quiet inside the park for many days.

With a startlingly explosive woof the old female ordered her cubs up the nearest tree. Nick dashed off with his small sister lagging behind. The cubs raced to the stump of a once giant oak tree that had been broken by a forgotten wind storm. All that was left of the tree was the dead gray stump ending in a jagged pinnacle among the leaves of other trees twenty feet above the ground. Around and around this limbless stump the cubs now spiraled toward its peak. Their mother assured herself that the cubs had taken refuge and, turning toward the approaching hounds, trotted off a hundred yards down the mountainside in their direction.

At other seasons, even the smallest of dogs might chase the largest of black bears beyond the nearest ridge, but this was a time of danger to her young. What she did not know was that on this day the hounds were not alone. Their owner was half trotting breathlessly along the mountain trail, trying vainly to keep up with his hounds.

Herb Gordon knew well that the old bears were on the mountains with their cubs at this season. And he also knew that there was a ready market for cubs. Down along the highway outside the park a cub in good condition would bring him two or three hundred dollars from roadside merchants who would house the bears in outdoor cages to attract the attention of passing tourists. Gordon figured that the way he was working it would be worth every penny of it if he caught a cub.

The four lean hounds reached the old she-bear fully ten minutes before their master came upon the scene. Facing the forest opening she saw them coming full force upon her position, their noses to the ground, their mouths open, their long red tongues hanging out in near exhaustion. They wailed in joyous anticipation as they drew closer. The lead dog in the pack slid to a stop in the leaves. His lips curled back, revealing long yellowish fangs. His baying had changed to sharp frantic barks and snarls. Meanwhile the old bear stood up to meet the hounds. The lead hound did not, understandably, dash in for the kill, but waited for his three companions to reach the scene.

Then with the four dogs around her in a snarling and yapping semicircle, the old bear dared them to close in for battle. Her lips curled back, revealing her own heavy, yellowed canines, which she snapped together repeatedly in a noisy warning. She growled at the hounds until one dared lunge at her flank. The hound had no chance to withdraw. She wheeled and struck in a single powerful motion and her sharp curving claws caught the dog in the soft underbelly as he was still in midair. With a vicious slashing she sent her claws through the soft flesh. As the dog fell screaming the old female rushed to him and crushed his skull between her teeth. Then she turned her attention to the remaining hounds.

Now, in sudden reconsideration, they fell back. The bear dropped to all fours and charged the nearest hound, but the dogs retreated so rapidly that even the old bear in her consuming fury could not catch them. Once again she stood on her hind legs and snarled, daring them to come to her. One of the three remaining hounds charged as the bear stood waiting, swinging her head and shoulders from side to side. And as surely as she had a few minutes before, the old she-bear delivered a blow to the second hound that dared take the risk. Half of Herb Gordon's pack of bear dogs now lay on the forest floor. One hound was already dead, the other fatally wounded.

Herb Gordon hurried along the shaded trail. The sharp anticipation of early profit spurred him on. At the first sound of the fight he knew what course the hunt had taken. A lone bear, he knew, would long since have led the hounds up and beyond the mountain. A wild hog, even a sow with young, would also have left the scene. Only the female bear taking care of her cubs might have stayed to fight.

At the precise moment that the enraged female sank her heavy canines into the soft neck of his third hound, Herb Gordon reached the scene of the fight. It had been so noisy that the man's arrival took the bear completely by surprise. She could handle the hounds, but this was a new threat, and one she knew that left her with no alternative. With Gordon's lone remaining hound yapping at her heels, the old bear backed into the tangle of the laurel slick. The bear was better able than the hound to push through the dense thicket, and the wall of tangled branches and greenbriar vines so frustrated the hound that he howled and squirmed about, losing valuable time in pursuit of the bear.

But the man had caught a glimpse of the cubs, and even before the female entered the thicket he was maneuvering himself into a position between her and her young.

Now from the elevated vantage point of his perch Nick saw the man coming around the edge of the laurel thicket. The cub was afraid. For many minutes he had not seen his mother, but had only heard her angry voice. He had listened to the yapping and snarling and death sounds of the dogs. The swaying and jerking of the tops of the bushes marked her progress as his mother continued to push her way through the laurel thicket.

But even before she emerged from the thick-growing mountain foliage, the man came struggling around the patch of laurel, stumbling over fallen logs, turning sideways to push himself and his clumsy shotgun through a tangle of greenbriar. Nick caught glimpses now of the great, black, familiar form of his mother coming closer and closer. He saw the man raise a long black object to his shoulder, and then, a new sound filled the forest. Nick flinched and ducked his head behind the stump. The first shot was followed by a second.

When Nick ventured again to stick his nose around the edge of the stump, a strange and unreal sight confronted him. His mother, the proud old she-bear, lay on her side, kicking feebly at the leaves. Fear and foreboding mounted in the cub. Nick whined and was torn between a desire to stay on the perch where his mother had ordered him and a growing urge to descend and run from the man and the dog.

Even as he looked down upon the scene, the man

and his dog ran to the base of the tree where the cubs had taken refuge. The yapping hound ran around the base of the tree. He leaped repeatedly as far as he could in his efforts to reach the cubs, but what the hound in his enthusiasm attempted he was incapable of accomplishing. Herb Gordon untied a piece of binder twine which secured two gunny sacks to his belt. Confronted with the almost certain double reward of twin cubs, Gordon was jubilant about his prospects for this day's work. Nick, edging closer and closer to the very peak of the stump, watched the preparations of the man below.

Gordon dropped the burlap bags and went a short distance into the woods, leaving the dog to keep the cubs treed. He came back carrying a twenty-foot sapling from which he trimmed the limbs and then he sharpened it to a point on its smaller end. Nick heard sounds coming from the man. "We'll take one at a time." He reached the pole up toward the cubs. "We'll get the little one first and leave the big feisty one for last."

Now the man punched the cub repeatedly with the sharpened end of the pole. The smaller cub squealed and whined and clung tightly to her perch. But time and again the sharp end of the pole dislodged her and forced her farther down the stump.

As she approached the bottom Gordon and his hound both closed in with deadly swiftness. Now the scrambling, flying paws of the frantic cub were trussed up together with rope, and her snout was shoved into the open mouth of one of the burlap bags. Quickly Gordon grabbed the edges of the bag and drew it over the cub and tied the bag shut with a piece of binder twine. Nick could no longer see his sister. All he could see was the strange shapeless brown form pitching and heaving among the leaves at the base of the tree.

Then the man once again picked up the long pole. Nick first swatted the pole away from him with his paw but soon he felt its sharp point punching at his soft haunches. Beneath him the hound kept up his continuous frightening yapping. The man poked him again and again. Nick scrambled to the top of the stump and attempted to perch there out of reach of this frightening new enemy, but no matter how he squeezed himself onto the narrow top of his tower he could not escape for long the punishing of the sharpened pole.

As he came down the tree rump first, around and around the trunk, Nick made a sudden maneuver that took both the man and the hound by surprise. Instead of continuing to let himself down the tree, the young cub, driven by confusion and fear, leaped from the stump. He thumped against the ground and rolled forward in the leaves. Both the man and the hound dived wildly at him, but Nick's reactions were lightning quick and before Gordon and his hound could recover their composure, he had a ten-foot start on them.

Running frantically up the mountainside, the young cub made a magnificent wild, lunging effort to escape his pursuers. Gordon was quickly left behind, but his age-old hate for all bears drove him to a final effort to stop the disappearing cub and cut off its dash for freedom. He brought the 12-gauge shotgun to his shoulder again. Nick, pushing his way through the undergrowth, heard the sound of the gun. Close beside him, the load of buckshot rattled through the leaves, and he veered in the opposite direction.

At his heels Gordon's hound closed in upon him. Nick had succeeded in leading the hound to a point beyond the reach of Gordon's gun. Frantic at the nearness of the hound, the cub raced once more for a tree. But the old hound, sensing this, cut in between Nick and the tree. Now Nick could yield to the fury of the attacking hound and perish, or he could stand and fight. Evading trouble was his nature, but he had no real choice.

In weight and size the hound and the cub were well matched. The hound rushed in and grabbed the cub by the soft fur over his shoulder. Then they separated and the cub, left with no path of escape, stood on his hind legs to meet the furious, frenzied attack of the hound. When they closed again, Nick scratched furiously at the dog's chest and then bit into his ear. He hung on to the ear as they rolled over in the leaves. The hound howled and tried to escape, and as he did, the cub's teeth ripped a long gash through his ear. Now the cowering hound had had his fill of bear fighting for one day, and he turned and ran to escape this ridiculously furious little black bear.

Blindly, Nick turned and dashed toward the depths

of the forest. He ran away from the man and the hound, and the place where his mother had died.

For several minutes he ran through the thick-growing underbrush. He sensed, eventually, that he was no longer being pursued by either the man or the hound. He was strangely alone in the forest for the first time in his life. This knowledge filled him with new terror.

He came to a well-traveled game trail that led him through the forest toward the top of the mountain. With no aim in mind and no purpose in his steps, he followed the trail.

Far below him, meanwhile, an angry man was plodding along another path with a brown sack across his shoulder. Herb Gordon was thinking. He wondered whether this hunt had been a good idea in the first place. The price of the single cub which he now smuggled out of the park had been three of his best hounds, a big price indeed to pay for one bear cub.

Chapter
8

*N*ick's life changed with a startling and shocking sud-
denness. Gone now was the great bear who had fed him
and sheltered him from the myriad threats facing a small
cub bear. Gone was the companionship of the other
cub. He wandered aimlessly along the trail beneath the
towering hardwoods. Here and there spots of brilliant
sunlight filtered through the forest canopy. But to Nick
the world about him did not seem one of peace and quiet.

He felt the dread loneliness of the helpless young in
an empire of predators. Familiar shadows in the forest
became threatening forms. He felt exposed to dangers
beyond his understanding and sensed an urgency to
hide. He walked away from the path and pushed deeper
into the undergrowth of the forest. Soon he stopped and
looked about. He lifted his nose, as he had so often seen
his mother do, and found no strange odors to alarm him.

He crept into the tangle of roots and branches and curled into a black ball to sleep.

Nick awakened abruptly. Somewhere in the trees above him the raucous alarm cry of a pair of bluejays pierced the woodlands. But sitting in his bed Nick detected no special threatening sounds or odors. And shortly the bluejays flew on, leaving only the buzzing of the insects and the melodious call of a nearby towhee. Rested now, the cub rose from his bed and wandered out of the patch of thicket that hid him.

Hours had passed since he last ate. He thought of his mother's milk and whimpered. Then he realized that the big bear was nowhere around. He began sniffing around the forest floor for items that might satisfy his hunger. He ate some bits of grass and chewed at the tender petals of some white violets he found.

Some combination of experience, instinct, and fear warned him to be silent, and surprisingly for a lost cub of Nick's age, he did not run whining through the woodlands attracting attention to his plight.

For a long time he wandered quietly and forlornly beneath the trees until darkness was falling over the blue-gray haze on the mountains. Trees cast long shadows far down the slopes and left the young bear in a world of half light. He came to the place where recent winds had brought a great white oak tree crashing to the ground. He forced his way into the wall of intertwined branches and lay down to sleep through the night.

When the first light of dawn filtered through a

dense wet fog, Nick was hungrier than ever. He turned down the trail again, perhaps because it was easier than going uphill.

He came to a small creek, and faint memories of other creeks came back to him. He had eaten bits of crayfish caught beneath rocks, and he had taken trout from the water. Now he sniffed about the creek and began turning over small rocks. On his third try he sent a big gray-brown crayfish scooting out from beneath his jabbing paw. It backed frantically into the middle of the shallow pool. Nick leaped into the water in sudden mad pursuit and joyously felt the splashing water around him as he scrambled in search of the crayfish. But the crayfish had eluded his clumsy amateur efforts, and Nick had so muddied the water that he could not see through it. Slowly he backed from the pool.

At the next pool, his luck improved. A green frog leaped from the bank and slipped beneath the cold surface of the water. Nick saw the amphibian dart under an overhanging bank. He sat down to study the situation and ponder how he might capture this creature. He leaned far over the bank and peered into the creek but could see no frog. Finally, with one mighty swat of his front paw he hit the place where he had seen the frog disappear. With more luck than skill, he impaled the frog in the mud. He brought the slippery creature to him and ate it.

Nick's hunger surpassed his food supply throughout this day and into the following one. He seemed unable,

without the guidance and help of his mother, to satisfy his gnawing belly.

The life of a cub alone in the forest is filled with risks. In addition to hunger, there is ever-present danger from free-running hounds. And should he escape these creatures, there are the old male bears who will quickly kill any cub caught alone in the forest.

On the next morning the cub left the trail and wandered through the woodlands until he came to the edge of the clearing left in the wake of an abandoned farm. The clearing was in the process of being reclaimed by the wilderness. Sumac mingled with the sassafrass, early invaders in the succession of forest plants that return the clearings to the forest. But what interested Nick immediately were the blackberry bushes. Only a few days earlier, with his mother and the other cub, he had fed on such berries. Now the bushes were bent heavy with fruit before his sniffing nose. He stood on his hind feet and picked berries.

He picked them one at a time with his sensitive lips, then swallowed them as fast as he could and did not bother to sort them from the leaves and twigs. He forgot the rest of the world around him. For the first time he forgot that he was alone and lost.

On the far side of the little clearing another animal paused to listen. Sounds made by the cub rustling in the bushes had reached sensitive ears. The animal stood until its broad head reared above the highest blackberry bush. Still unable to see the small black cub, the creature dropped to all four feet and moved boldly forward to a better vantage point. Once again it stood high on its hind legs and this time the cub, busy at his berry picking, came into view.

The observer was a lone female bear. At about the time of Nick's birth the preceding winter, this female had given birth to a single cub. Together they had wandered unharmed through the weeks of early spring and into the warm days of July. But more than twenty-four hours had passed since she had led her cub out of the woods and along the edge of the highway. As she frequently did, this female had walked across the road, expecting that her cub would be close at her heels. But the cub lagged back in the darkness of the roadside and when he began to trot across the highway to join his mother, a speeding car with two brilliant white headlights came charging out of the night. The blinded cub stood confused in the middle of the road—a black spot on a black highway. Squealing brakes applied at the last moment could not save him. After the automobile had gone, the female returned to touch her nose gently to the still form of her small dead cub. The following day she wandered off alone into the forest.

Now the young female looked about for the mother of the cub, but did not see another bear. The only bears in the clearing were the small cub in its first summer and the female. She stood motionless for a time.

Nick held back. No animal in all his experience had earned his trust except his own mother and the other cubs. Yet for some reason he refrained from backing off into the woods to hide from the older animal. He stood comically moving his little head from side to side, sniffing. And once or twice he whined, as he had not done for almost two days and nights. Nick felt a strong urge to go to the female. Then, as if she had completed her investigation, the young female turned her back on the cub. Ignoring his gentle pleading look, she wandered away toward her own side of the berry patch.

He watched her form blend into the underbrush. Irresistibly, Nick found himself moving forward. He followed the larger bear, but kept a respectable distance behind her. After eating as many berries as they could find, the two bears left the clearing and went back to the safety of the timberlands. The female knew the cub was behind her, and she made no effort to elude the smaller animal or to chase him off.

The cub followed the young female until she found a bedding area in the dense undergrowth. She lay down and curled up to rest, and the cub crept close. The she-bear raised her head once to look at him as he settled on the leaves, watching her closely. Her mammary glands were heavy with the milk for her first-born and she permitted this strange cub to nurse.

In the days that followed, the older bear accepted her role as the cub's teacher and protector. Nick had a foster mother, and the female had a new cub of her own. In the company of the large bear Nick was never threatened by other bears, and she resumed his lessons on finding food and selecting the best hiding places.

Together they tore apart rotting logs to find ants, dug roots, stole honey from farm apiaries, and frequently raided garbage cans in the nearby campgrounds to obtain free food from the vacationing campers. This was a new experience for Nick.

His first visit to a campground came a few weeks after he joined the young female. The two of them came from the woods in the evening and padded to the edge of the campground. The noise, confusion, and proximity of so many people brought a great sense of dread and fear to the cub. Dim memories of the hounds and Gordon's gun swept in upon him. He sat where he believed himself hidden at the edge of the underbrush, but to his surprise his foster mother went quite boldly into the middle of the campground. He saw her put her front feet to the top of a garbage can and poke her head far down in the container. She came up with a paper sack and carried it in her mouth back to the edge of the woods where he waited. With a single swipe of her powerful claws she slashed open the sack and scattered paper and soggy coffee grounds along with scraps of egg, meat, and pastry on the ground. Some of these tasted good to Nick.

The following day as the female once more led the way back to the camping area, Nick felt a quickening anticipation. His fears of people and their works were gradually being overcome by a desire for the food to be found where people lived. This time Nick followed the female into the campground, and almost immediately he attracted the attention of a group of campers.

The closer they came to him, the tighter Nick tried to stick to the bigger bear. That creature, as it shortly developed, was turning her interest away from the garbage can and in another direction.

Nearby, a picnicking family had just spread a meal on the table and the older bear went to it without hesitation. The people yelled at her, but she did not go away. Instead she stood up and put her front paws on the edge of the red and white checked tablecloth. At this, the campers scrambled quickly away, falling over each other in their haste.

The bear swept all the items within arm's reach from the table. A bottle of cola fell to the ground and rolled in a crazy irregular circle, coming to a stop at Nick's feet. He put his nose down to investigate the brown liquid that gurgled from the container and promptly tasted it. Its sweet bubbly effervescence came as a wonderful surprise. It was the best-tasting water he had ever found. He pushed the rolling bottle with his paws but it was empty and most of it had soaked into the ground.

Suddenly he looked up to find the older bear gone. She had grabbed up a cake covered with marshmallow icing and was loping toward the woods. Nick ran as fast as his short legs would go to close the distance between himself and the disappearing rump of the she-bear. He forgot about the yelling of the people who milled about the campground.

Chapter
9

The snows had melted and the hills had awakened to the next spring's wet, insistent urging. The grass was green around the Swope place. In June, the ox-eye daisies speckled the pasture fields with white and yellow, and the mountain laurel's pink blossoms had come and were almost gone. Luther Swope came in one evening from the chores with a welcome suggestion. After the supper table was cleared, the Swopes bumped up the brown, rutted lane to the country road in their little truck. Half an hour later they sat high up in the back row of the outdoor amphitheater looking down over the heads of tourist families. The park naturalist was ready to begin his talk and show his slides of the Great Smoky Mountains.

"The earliest white men to view these mountains," the naturalist explained, "and perhaps the red man before, called them the Smokies because of the haze that hangs over the peaks and ridges, like a thin film of blue-

gray smoke. And if you wonder where it comes from—
what causes the haze on the mountains—you are looking
at the reason. This vegetation that grows so abundantly
and vigorously here gives off the moisture. And the
vapor is the 'smoke' of the Great Smokies."

Although he had heard it before, Johnny still wondered if he should believe what they said about the
trees. "If you include the smaller species," said the naturalist, "there are more than a hundred kinds of trees
growing within the park. And there are thirteen hundred
species of flowering plants."

He explained that the park covers eight hundred
square miles. How big is eight hundred square miles?
From east to west the park extends for fifty-four miles,
and it measures fifteen miles across from north to south.
For thirty-six miles the high ridge of the mountains
stand more than five thousand feet—a mile—above sea
level. This ridgeline, the border between Tennessee and
North Carolina, is the backbone of the Smokies, and the
hollows off it are the ribs. More than six hundred miles
of streams, mostly steep, narrow, and turbulent, carry
water from the rains and melting snow down these long
slopes and high peaks out of the mountains to the big
rivers and lakes beyond.

From the floor of the valleys to the distant peaks the
quantities of rain and snow during a year's time increase
with the altitude. "During the summer months," the naturalist explained, "it may rain every day or two in these
mountains."

Eventually he came to the part of his talk John most wanted to hear, the part about the bears. "There are probably between three hundred and four hundred bears living in the park," he said. "Nobody has ever figured out a good way to count them, but we think this figure is close. And in summertime, most of the bear population lives along the highways.

"Just as the signs say," he added, "it is against the law to feed the bears. There are excellent reasons. One reason is for the welfare of the bears. This is a nature preserve and we try to keep the wildlife wild, for future generations. Wild bears can find their own food, providing we do not destroy the forest which is their natural habitat. But bears are intelligent enough and adaptable enough to live on handouts. Once they have acquired these lazy habits, they teach their cubs that food is easily secured along the highways. And they lead their cubs to all the garbage cans, and sometimes to the cars and tents as well, in search of food.

"If rangers chase the bears away, it is not to keep visitors from seeing bears. It is more to keep bears from begging and creating traffic hazards.

"The second reason we are concerned about feeding the bears is the safety of the folks who feed them. Bears are playful animals by nature, but they do not understand teasing.

"Already this year we had a man sent to the hospital. He had to have his arm sewed up where a bear cut two gashes twenty inches long. Was the bear vicious?

74

Not really. The man offered the bear a slice of bread and peanut butter and the bear reached for it. Then the man drew the bread back. Before he knew what was happening, the bear slashed him.

"But whether it is the bear's fault or not, if we know which bear is involved, we haul him away. If he gets into more trouble we have to dispose of him. It's safest to watch the bears from behind the closed windows of your cars. And be especially careful around females with cubs. The female black bear is among the best of all wild mothers, and she will fight ferociously to protect her young."

Toward the close of his talk the naturalist said, "Most adult black bears weigh from 150 to 225 pounds. An average adult will weigh perhaps 175 pounds, stand about three and a half feet high at the shoulders, and is able to reach to a height of seven and a half feet if he stands on his hind feet. They do not, incidentally, hug people to death.

"Sometimes, just as you find among people, there is a bear that is especially big. We have one around this campground that seems headed for the record books if he keeps growing. Right now he's only a year and a half old but already he's nearly as big as the adults. You've probably seen him if you've been here a few days. If you pay attention to the bear's tracks, you'll see that this one has two middle toes missing from the right front foot."

The following afternoon Luther was not surprised when John asked if he could quit hoeing early and go fishing for trout in Spicer Creek. He cast a half-amused glance at the boy whose hoe was chopping morning glory vines at a great rate. "It'll be all right," he said, "just make sure you're back in time for supper."

John cleaned the clay from his hoe and hung it in its place in the apple tree outside the kitchen door. He went to his room and came out with his spinning rod and reel. "I'm going to dig some worms to take along," he told his mother.

She looked up from the table where she was packing green peas into scalded glass jars for winter meals. "All right, Johnny," she said. "You remember when supper time comes, and be back in time to help your daddy with the feedin'."

She followed her son to the kitchen door. "And if you should by any stretch of the imagination," she added lightly, "get as far as the park, don't try feedin' the bears. You remember what the man said?" John remembered.

From Swope's to the campground was eight miles by road, but it was less than two miles across the mountains.

John dug a few worms in the moist soil beside the watering trough, then drank heavily from the spring water trickling through the pipe in its never-ceasing stream.

Johnny followed Spicer Creek. Upstream a few hundred yards he came to his favorite fishing hole. Few people ever came here to fish. Mr. Gordon knew about it, but Herb Gordon never had time for fishing. His father knew about it, and once or maybe twice each summer he came here with John.

The boy eased himself through the thicket beside the creek until he was upstream above the hole. He impaled a red worm on the small hook he had tied to his monofilament line. Then, creeping forward slowly to the edge of the pool, he made an easy, flicking cast of the bait and watched it fall into the upper edge of the riffle at the foot of the fishing hole.

The line slipped off the reel and ran freely between his fingers as the current carried the tumbling worm downstream along the bottom of the creek. He felt the weight of the fish the moment it touched the bait. He let the fish go a few feet and pause in its brief run, then he set the hook with a sharp upward motion of his rod tip.

It is one thing to hook a vigorous rainbow trout, and sometimes another to bring him to the shore. Many times John had lost trout such as this one. So now he thought of nothing else. For this moment he even forgot the big bear. His full attention was on the beautiful fish leaping from the frothing eddy. Alert to every pressure on the line, the boy waited each time until the fish had reached the peak of its leap. Then with a turn of his wrist, he tipped it off balance to maintain the tension on his line.

Soon he brought the fish to the bank and, holding the rod high with his left hand, leaned down and scooped the rainbow from the water with his other hand.

He held it and admired it. Maybe he could catch another. They would make a fine dinner.

He cast a few more times into the pool but no trout picked up the tumbling bait. Farther upstream he came to a second hole, which, like the first, was fed from a riffle above and emptied by a riffle below. Here he caught his second fish, only slightly smaller than the first. Any other day he would have stayed in the shade of the laurel growing by the creek and tried to add more trout to his stringer. But on this day fishing had been only an excuse for a still bigger adventure. He picked up his rod and his trout and left Spicer Creek behind. He made a short cut through the woods and hiked uphill toward the park campground.

Where his trail intercepted the one he intended to follow home, John hung his rod upside down in the branches of a beech tree and tied the fish to a limb, where they revolved slowly in the shade.

Every space in the campground seemed to John to be filled with people. He felt crowded, more crowded than he liked to be. There were tents and trailers and trailers that were half tent and half trailer. There were children of all ages running in every direction, and mothers yelling at them and fathers trying to look relaxed in the shade. John walked unnoticed between two tents and turned down the camp lane toward the main highway.

He passed through the campground and hiked on. But still he saw no bears. As he came to the main road, however, he saw several cars stopped a hundred yards down the hill. That's where the bears would be. The rangers, he knew, would call this a "bear jam." A bear beside the road was frequently enough to back up automobiles for a mile or more. Sometimes the hills were alive with the angry clamor of their horns.

John squeezed into the crowd until he could see the bear. "He couldn't be Nick," John thought to himself, "because he's just plain too big. The man said 'big,' but he didn't say *that* big." The big bear sat on his haunches like a fat man on a milking stool and coolly surveyed each face in the circle around him. John thought at first that this must be some elderly creature among the bears, a king of his kind, with most of his life already behind him. But the boy looked carefully now at the face of the big black bear. In spite of its size, this bear was youthful. His brow was unfurrowed, and the fur on his face was jet black to the tips.

Now the bear sat up, as experience had taught him, and waited until one of the people might offer him food or drink. Unlike some bears, however, this one kept his audience where he could see everyone. If people tried to go behind him, he lowered his bulk to all four feet and moved back toward the safety of the woods. Even to gain the human being's favor, his native caution had not been completely sacrificed.

The bear turned then and looked directly at John, his paws extended. John caught his breath. There was a wide gap in the middle of the bear's right foot. The two middle claws were missing. John's remaining question was one that had haunted him since the previous evening when he first suspected that Nick might be living around the campground. Would this wild creature, which he had rescued from the trap, fed, and cared for as best he knew how, remember him? Some bears have good memories, and smells, especially, make lasting impressions upon their minds.

A tourist dressed in red shorts moved toward Nick, holding out a Coke for him to take. "This is the one that likes Cokes," she said. Nick took the Coke, and in so doing brought his claws within an inch of the woman's fingers. The bear clamped the bottle firmly between his broad pads and lifted it to his lips. He drank noisily and the brown liquid gurgled down his throat, outside and inside, until the bottle was empty, while joyful campers took uncounted photographs. Nick carelessly dropped the bottle to the ground.

The bear dropped to all fours again, and now John, even though he knew better, began moving closer and closer to the youthful black giant. It was as if some force prompted him to learn the truth. He spoke softly to the bear. His motions were the smooth actions of the mountain man who understands the fears of wild creatures. At a distance of ten feet Nick looked up into John's face. "Easy, Nick. Remember me? Come here, boy. Come see me, Nick. It's all right. Remember?" The bear took one step toward the boy. John sensed that the crowd was backing away behind him.

"Boy, you better get back there," some unknown male voice behind him warned. But instead of giving ground, John took one more step toward the bear. Now the crowd stood silent, staring transfixed at the strange sight of the boy and the bear, advancing on each other.

When he stood no more than arm's length from the bear's nose, John stopped and waited to see now what Nick would do. He felt he had to know. He wanted the answer to his question. Here before him was the only bear he had ever made friends with, the only cub he had ever kept.

Nick had lifted his nose high now, almost to the shoulder level of the gangling boy in front of him, and was sniffing repeatedly. "I'll bet you do know, don't you?" John said. He reached out a hand and let the bear sniff his fingers. Nick made no motion either to escape or swing on John's hand as he almost certainly would have done with another person. He only continued to sniff in investigation.

Perhaps it was fortunate for John that at this moment a ranger's car appeared, moving slowly around the curve in the highway. John had given no thought to how he might get away from the bear if Nick did not recognize him, or even whether or not the bear might follow him. The ranger solved his problem.

At the sound of the ranger's voice and the sight of his car, Nick quickly turned and vanished in the woods behind him. "We'll have to move the cars along," the ranger said. "Traffic's blocked all down the hill."

"You should have been here a minute ago," one of the crowd said. "That boy was petting the big bear that drinks Cokes."

"What boy?" asked the ranger seriously.

"Why, the one right here . . ." Not only was Nick gone, but Johnny had vanished too. John had no idea what the ranger would say about his petting a bear, or whether he would report him to his father, but he did not intend to find out. With the stealth of a deer stalker, he dodged from shadow to shadow until the campground, the highway, and the crowd were out of sight behind him. A short time later he found his fishing rod and trout and turned toward home.

Chapter
10

During that summer and the following one, Nick's reputation grew around the national park. His antics brought mixed reactions of hilarity and anger to the human population, depending upon how directly the people were involved. Nick seemed somehow to avoid detection by the rangers even when up to his most destructive tricks.

Most of the time the big bear would be in the woods sleeping, but at least once a day, usually in the early evening, he would put in an appearance around some camping area. For a while he might sit on his haunches near the edge of the woods and carefully survey the situation, giving the impression that he had no cares on earth. Outwardly his intentions appeared to be the best, and his countenance reflected nothing but a charming brand of elusive wilderness innocence. Viewed in these quiet moments Nick was indeed a big, lovable creature and a pleasure to visitor and ranger alike.

But what the people came gradually to realize was that Nick never sat innocently on the sidelines for long. In fact, it began to appear that these rest periods were only times of planning and that while he sat he was looking for the most satisfactory way to create maximum trouble without getting caught in the act.

Early in his second summer, shortly after his foster mother abandoned him in favor of a truculent male bear in search of a mate, Nick discovered an effective method of chasing picnickers from their tables, a method he may have discovered by accident. One day when every picnic table in the area seemed occupied by a family of visitors, Nick climbed to the first branches of a red oak tree. Below him and off to one side he could look down on the food and activities of a family that had arrived shortly after he did. As Nick looked at the food, the people looked nervously up at him.

Then, drawn by the rich smells, Nick balanced himself precariously and worked himself out on the swaying limb until he was over the table. The people scurried away from the table. Below him, scarcely four feet away, was more food than any one bear might hope to eat at a single sitting. The farther he moved out on the branch, the more it dipped, and he hardly had to leap at all, but simply stepped onto the heavily laden table. He stood there and looked first at one offering, then another. He decided on a whole roast chicken, took it in his mouth and, jumping from the table, waddled toward the woods and made good his escape. When he returned to the tree some days later, the branch had been sawed off and hauled away.

During the summer he learned that tents and automobiles were likely places for people to store their food. He learned to sniff around every camp shelter or vacationer's vehicle he encountered and developed into a specialist at breaking into automobiles.

There was, for example, the small convertible he found one night. Nick walked through the dark campground and around a canvas-topped camper-trailer. He could hear the deep breathing of the campers asleep inside. A few yards away he came to the automobile. He walked around it slowly and sniffed with growing interest. From inside the car came the odors of meat, butter, and fruit, and the food cooler sat in the middle of the front seat.

Nick raised himself and rested his front feet on the low hood of the car. He lifted a rear foot up and deftly hoisted his bulk; the metal sagged beneath his weight. The unsteadiness of his support made the bear nervous, and for a few seconds he stood waiting to see what would develop. Then, with renewed courage, he lifted his front paws to the roof of the convertible, and stood there sniffing first to one side then the other. The odors coming to his sensitive nostrils were very strong now. Beneath his broad padded feet the roof of the car felt softer than the logs he could so easily rip apart. He extended his front foot far out in front of him and with a burst of wild speed slashed three long gashes in the car-top. He caught the tips of his claws in the edge of the severed material and with a sidewise heave of his shoulders tore away half the car's top.

He let himself down into the car beside the food cooler and tore away the lid of the ice box, ripping it off its hinges. He did not linger there to eat, but instead picked up a pound of bacon and made good his escape into the forest before the campers nearby knew what he had done.

Nick's fascination with the contents of automobiles increased through the remaining months of the tourist season and carried over into the following summer as well. Most of the food he consumed now came the easy way; he gleaned it from the campgrounds where people concentrated, and there was hardly any place they might hide food without having it discovered. Each time he felt hunger pangs, he automatically turned toward the campground. Late in the afternoon of one of these summer days he awakened to the insistent growling of his demanding stomach. For a brief time he sat in his bed in the laurel thicket and stretched and yawned. Then the youthful giant rose silently to his feet and waddled off toward the campground, from which he could now plainly hear the sounds of vacationing humans half a mile farther up the mountainside.

Some automobiles, as Nick learned one night a few weeks later, are more difficult to get into than those with soft tops. He came late in the night to the heart of the campground when everything was quiet. He followed his nose to some strong cheese in a cardboard box securely locked in the trunk of a car. With one crashing blow of his paw he smashed open the window of the car. But the hole was too small for him, and he hooked his claws over the edge of the door and pulled with all the strength he could muster. The lock broke loose and the door swung open so hard Nick fell over on his back in a ludicrous heap. He proceeded to crawl into the car but he could find the food nowhere. In the back seat the odor was stronger and he pulled apart the upholstery. Then he broke through the thin partition into the trunk. Here his persistence was finally rewarded. With the pound of cheese firmly in his jaws, he left the scene of his mischief.

Early the following month another camping family made the mistake of setting a food box inside the tent. An ordinary bear would have had no trouble solving this problem; Nick just happened to be the first bear to reach the tent and track down the source of the attractive aroma. The canvas tent yielded like tissue before his claws. But at the moment his brown snout protruded into the tent, a hiking boot came crashing across his sensitive nose. With an explosive woof, the bear backed out of the tent. He stood a dozen feet away staring dolefully at the human faces that came to the rip he had cut in the canvas. The shaken campers threw out the food box as ransom for their lives. The bear ignored it and ran off to the woods. Behind him the campers tore down their damaged tent, packed everything into their car, and vanished into the night.

One afternoon he arrived when no other bears had been around for many hours. The campers had enjoyed a relatively quiet day. Some, in fact, claimed it was getting dull and they wished the bears would come. It is true that these bored souls might have gone fishing in the nearby trout streams, or they might have gone hiking, as the foot trails lead to the most beautiful timbered wilderness in the eastern half of their land. But they preferred instead on this day to sit in their folding camp chairs and wait for nature, in the form of bears, to come to them. The national park and the federal government that administered it seemed to owe them that much.

Nick did not wander immediately into the heart of the big campground. Instead he stopped frequently, as was his custom, and sized up the situation. At the edge of the timber he stopped and looked through the leafy curtain at the scene beyond.

Nick stood for several minutes moving his head first one way then the other. He tested the air, then tested it again. He tried to sort out the many odors and determine which he would follow. Finally, catching the faint smell of some fascinating edible ahead of him and off to the right, he followed his nose. Sometimes his nose led him to food, sometimes to trouble, and sometimes both. What he smelled now was a pan of meat loaf on the front seat of a red sports car parked on a hill at the edge of the campground. The little car was so low that Nick could almost see over the door without standing up. The top had been rolled down. Beyond the car, asleep on two air mattresses in the shade of the spruce trees, lay the couple who had come in the car to spend the day.

For an accomplished young bear, this was almost too easy. Nick nimbly crawled over the door of the little red compact and squatted down in the bucket seat. He grabbed the pan of meat loaf. With the pan in his mouth, he turned to crawl back from the car to the ground, and as he did so his forearm bumped a small lever on the floor.

A moment later Nick, seated behind the steering wheel, stared around in confused disbelief. For the first time in his life, the trees were running past *him*. And they were going faster and faster. The sports car with the bear in the seat swerved from one side to the other and then careened into the campground and crashed through an unoccupied tent. The jolt turned the car back toward the camp road, and Nick leaped out and rolled over and over as he hit the ground. The car traveled another fifty feet and crashed head-on into an oak tree. It was so badly damaged that it had to be towed down the mountainside.

Through the following days the story spread throughout the national park. It grew with each new telling. Meanwhile, the bear, still unidentified, had long since taken refuge in the forest.

Chapter
11

*During June of his fourth year Nick felt the awaken-*ing of an interest in the female black bears within his territory. For some weeks his male reproductive glands, dormant so much of the year, had undergone gradual development. Females still nursing their young of the previous winter would not develop the mating urge until the following summer, but females which were not lactating were approaching mating condition and were sending their year-and-a-half-old cubs away on their own.

These large youthful cubs seemed highly confused by the whole turn of events. Suddenly, without apparent reason, their mothers refused to defend them. Eventually the yearling cubs wandered off through the woods, stopping occasionally to look hopefully back at their sullen mothers. But the family ties had at last been completely severed.

Nick came one evening upon the trail of a female

who had recently disowned her large twin cubs. Her smell filled him with excitement, and a new sense of urgency made him forget his search for food. With quickened pace, he trotted along the trail the female had followed.

A short while later he arrived at the place where the female was nonchalantly digging at pieces of a rotting log she was taking apart. Nick approached her as if not quite certain of his reception. The female heard him and looked up as he approached. She lifted her head and sniffed the air before returning to her work with the log. Nick, meanwhile, continued to move in closer until scarcely five feet separated him from the female. Compared to Nick she was a small animal and not impressive looking. But Nick was impressed. Tentatively, he began helping her tear the log apart. She neither encouraged nor reproached him, but seemed to pay him only the slightest attention. Then apparently tired of it all, she turned and walked away. Nick walked behind her.

In the hours that followed, the female took increasing notice of the big, youthful bear's presence. He stayed very close to her. She paused once and seemed to find no objection when he rubbed the side of her neck and head with his nose. These evidences of affection continued from time to time. Throughout the night the presence of the female bear quickly became the only matter of importance in the big male's world, and this was his mood at the first light of dawn when a bellowing roar made him suddenly aware of the presence of another male.

The bear came upon them from behind to find that the female he had trailed was not alone. Nick saw him for the first time standing there on his hind feet, his teeth bared and clicking in belligerent challenge.

In that instant, rage charged through every fiber of Nick's great body. The night had been quiet and few things had disturbed this wondrous period with the female. Then in an instant this creature had changed it all. The older bear was almost as large as Nick, and what he lacked in size was compensated for in meanness and a temper soured by toothache and pains of bone and muscle.

But now, as in no other time before in his life, Nick had come to appreciate his place in the world of forest wild creatures. His temper and determination were reinforced by his magnificient strength and his youth. The roar that issued from him made even the older animal seem to tremble.

Nick rushed forward, and as he and the other bear met he rose to his full height. The forest monsters snarled and turned their heads sideways in efforts to rip through the hide and fat layer of each other with their bared teeth.

Nick slashed a long raking claw mark across the chest of the old bear, who bellowed and flailed wildly at his antagonist. But Nick dodged and broke through the old bear's defenses, slashing repeatedly at the animal's bulk. Trails of blood marked the path of his claws. With each puncture he made, Nick put the incredible power of his arms and shoulders behind the raking hooked claws on his feet.

Such fights more often than not come to a harmless end before they have progressed far. This fight between Nick and the old stranger was the exception. The strongest of urges prompted it, and the individual characters of these two kept it going until one bear could fight no longer.

After more than half an hour of fighting, Nick made a last powerful lunge and closed in to grapple with the panting old monarch. So deep did he cut the bear that he touched vital organs. This coupled with the continuous flow of blood weakened the old one and he sagged slowly to the ground, where a moment later he lay dead.

Nick made one final, halfhearted swipe at the side of the broad, motionless head, but he realized that there was no longer danger of competition from the bear lying stretched out so still on the scuffed earth. His task completed, he turned again to find the female. He had not come through without gashes of his own, but these scars of battle would soon heal. He was still sound of wind and strong of muscle. And he was a king now by his own efforts.

He stood on his hind legs and, looking about him in the dim light as if to seek out and challenge any other lurking competitors, he growled. He took a few steps in this upright position, his great bloodied paws dangling before him. But he dropped to all four feet and made his way quickly up the slope to the female, who was digging beneath the rocks on the edge of a spring as if she neither knew nor cared that the two biggest giants of the forest had just completed a battle to the death to see which should possess her.

The victory did not turn Nick into more of a killer than he had been before, although the old bear was the first one of his own kind he had ever killed. This episode had been the rare but natural outcome of circumstances. For Nick it was done, and it was soon forgotten.

For six days and nights Nick and the female traveled together. Instead of visiting the campgrounds and the garbage cans, they chose to wander through the deepest forests.

Along the bear trails they came one day to a small cedar tree bearing the tooth marks of other bears. When Nick found this tree he stood up to his full height. His custom was always the same at the bear-sign tree. He stood for a moment rubbing the highest tooth marks of the previous bears. He rubbed the marks with the under-

side of his chin. Then stretching to his full height, he bit chunks from the soft bark of the cedar as if daring any other bear in all the forest to mark the tree higher. His marks were three inches higher than any others.

Nick and the female slept during the days. At night they fed and wandered wherever the trails led them through the moist forest now rich with the abundance of early summer's luxuriant growth. And there were times when they were interested not in the rest of the world around them, but only in each other. They sometimes stood on their hind legs, and sparred like cubs or, reaching out affectionately, touched each other's fur softly.

But the mating time of the bears is quickly ended. The female began to lose interest in Nick and they wandered farther and farther apart, until without emotion or even knowledge of the parting, they fed one night in different directions. That was the last time they saw each other.

Except for the unpredictable events ahead, Nick might have found still another mate in the days to come. He had hunted through much of the night, but without great success, and toward morning he curled up in the density of a tangled rhododendron thicket to sleep.

If he had fed heavily he might have slept through the day, but early in the afternoon he sat up in his bed to heed the rumbling of his stomach. He yawned and after a few minutes rose slowly to his feet. He walked from the place where he had bedded and pushed his bulk into one of the runs that the bears had tunneled through the tangled brush of the thicket.

Away from the slick, he walked slowly across the steep slope in the direction of a picnic ground, guided by the sounds of laughter and human voices. A short time later he sat at the shaded edge of the clearing waiting for whatever might happen next. Then someone saw him. A shrill human voice cried, "There's a big one! Look at that big one!" Now, as they had so often done before, people began to move toward Nick. And they held out offerings.

Such items as were edible Nick would take, but the only delicacy that reduced him to active begging was a bottle of soft drink. At the sharp memory of the delightful sensation caused by the sweet bubbling water in his mouth, Nick would sit up and hold out both of his great powerful paws in request. Often someone in the crowd would understand.

Then Nick saw a small girl in the back seat of a nearby automobile. The child leaning on the edge of the open window did not understand that the bottle of pop in her hand held particular appeal to this bear. Nick moved heavily toward the car. He stopped close beside it and sat up. Once more he extended his paws for the soft drink. Around him the familiar cameras clicked with mechanical monotony. But inside the car the child, frightened by the bear's advance, scrambled to the far side of the seat.

With her she took the bottle of pop. Nick now reached in for the prize being withdrawn, and he did not reach gently. With lightning swiftness he brought his gigantic paw with its curved claws sweeping downward upon the bottle.

He missed the bottle and the small hand that held it by a fraction of a second and a fraction of an inch. His dark face with its bottomless, expressionless eyes, now peered into the window at the terror-stricken child who cowered, speechless, in the far corner of the car.

Her father, behind the wheel, finally got the car started. It lurched forward, spilling Nick into the road. He stood there looking after the car.

The car screeched to a stop again as a green pickup truck driven by the park ranger rounded the curve. Nick distrusted the rangers who rode in these little trucks. Never could he recall having been given food by them. Instead, long experience had taught Nick that the men in the truck would chase bears off into the woods. No longer did he wait to see what would now develop. Where people had a few minutes ago meant the promise of food and treats, their presence now carried the threat of danger, and it is the nature of wild creatures to attempt escape from situations they do not understand.

"You have to kill that bear!" The woman was almost as hysterical now as her small daughter. "You have to kill that bear, the giant one, the big black one. He tried to kill our little girl! He tried to get her out of the car. You have to kill him, do you hear? You have to kill him!"

For the next half hour the ranger talked with those who had witnessed the event. Eventually he felt that he understood what had actually happened. He searched the dust at the edge of the road. Now he knew which bear it was. "Well, Three Toes," he said, "you're going on a trip."

Chapter
12

A few miles away two workmen were putting the final touches on a device designed to bring an end to Nick's mischief. The rangers who were making a trap for Nick were guided by a directive that had come from the national capital. To all its parks where bears were prominent attractions, the National Park Service had issued the same guiding order. "The black bear is native to much of the United States," said the paper, "and several areas of the national park system have well-established populations. Originally the bears were self-reliant, but over a period of years many have lost this desirable trait.

"Because of man-made causes, the bear in certain areas has become a nuisance animal. This condition is one of long standing. We must remember that the park visitor is entitled to the privilege of viewing this animal in the wild and not as it feeds in garbage cans or at the traffic hazard 'bear jams' along scenic highways.

"In addition we have an obligation to provide reasonable protection for the public against personal injury, and for the welfare of the bears.

"Once the spoiled bears are removed and those practices or conditions responsible for the spoiling corrected, we can then keep the wild population wild. Those bears that still develop bad habits will have to be removed. Remove habitual beggars and those that damage property in search of food. Live-trapping is a well-established method. Those that return after having been hauled away once must be dealt with promptly and effectively. Remove by shooting those identifiable rogue bears that cannot be successfully transplanted."

The trap being made ready in the park service area was a section of heavy steel culvert pipe three feet in diameter and eight feet long. The men welded a steel wall in one end. There were small holes drilled through the steel for ventilation.

Next they constructed a heavy steel door at the other end. This door was arranged to fall straight down by following tracks. Although the trap's designer spoke of the door as a "guillotine door," it was not built to remove the head of its victim, but to cut off his freedom.

Inside the tunnel-like structure a long rod was fastened into place. Onto this was welded a trigger to which a bait would be attached. Next the trap was lifted onto a frame supported on wheels and bolted down to become an oddly shaped trailer with but a single purpose—to catch and carry away those bears that the rangers believed could no longer get along with people.

One morning shortly after the trap was built, two men hitched it to the back of a pickup truck. They towed it out of the shop and down the lane toward the highway. There the driver turned south.

The pickup truck turned into the campground and at the far side of the area came to a halt where a metal pipe from one post to another barred the entrance to a forest service road. The men unlocked the padlock, drove through, and locked it again behind them. They hauled the bear trap half a mile into the woods, where few campers ever came.

The two workmen parked the truck and hiked along the trail. They found the crossing they wanted for the trap, and after a few minutes of maneuvering, had the trailer backed into position.

They removed shovels from the bed of the truck and began digging trenches behind the wheels of the trailer. When the trenches were twelve inches deep, the driver backed the pickup truck until the trailer wheels settled into the newly dug pits. The men stood now inspecting their work. The bottom of the tubelike trap rested a few inches above the ground. "That should make it real easy for him," one of them said. "It'll be almost no effort at all for him to get caught."

The workmen shoveled dirt and leaves into the trap and spread them over the floor. Now they unhitched the trailer and its trap. One man crawled into the trap and tied a one-pound piece of beef onto the trigger.

Then, the guillotine door was set so that only the trigger mechanism supported it. Although it was probably not necessary, and might not have helped fool a bear, they leaned a few pieces of brush against the side of the trap to break its outline. They stood back now to check their work; they had forgotten nothing. They drove their truck away and left the trap to the bears.

Nick started toward the campgrounds shortly before dark, as was his custom. On the way from the woods he stopped, looked at the strange contraption, and sniffed the air. Then he walked on, thinking only of the free meal waiting at the campground nearby.

He came to the trap again late in the night on his return trip to the forest, but now he was well fed and once more he ignored the offering. Half an hour behind him, however, a smaller bear came padding along the trail from the campground. He stopped and sniffed around the trap and savored the wonderful odor of the meat. Moving cautiously, he crawled into the tunnel. He paused and sniffed as he went forward. He took the meat in his teeth and started to leave. The heavy steel door clattered down behind him. The small bear wheeled and faced the door. He clawed it but could not make it open.

After many hours he heard the sound of the pickup truck.

He lifted his head when he saw the man peering through the bars on the door. He heard the sounds of the man. "It's not the one we're after. This one's littler." Shortly the smaller bear was released, and he ran into the forest.

Behind him the men once more set the trap, and departed in their truck. Throughout that day the trap remained empty. The men would not come again until the following morning.

In the early evening Nick came from the woods. He walked in his plodding, deliberate manner, swinging his weight from side to side, stopping now and again to test the breezes. Then he came to the trap.

Nick stopped this time and looked more carefully at the trap. He had spent much of the day asleep, and hunger was strong within him. He sniffed all around the base of the trap. And he came then to the entrance.

Now the rich odor of the meat reached his nostrils and he sniffed several times. The smell from inside the tunnel was enticing, but Nick was cautious. In all his months of association with people and their devices he had never come to trust them. He took what they offered without losing his own independence. Candy bars, cookies, hot dogs, and marshmallows had never completely extinguished his wild nature. He felt uneasy about having his head and shoulders inside this strange thing. He could see very little in the semidarkness. Even though

the meat attracted him, Nick withdrew from the trap. He backed into the light of evening again and stood at the entrance of the trap looking all about him.

He turned as if to walk back to the trail that led to the campground. But then he stopped again and turned back to the trap. Once more he put his head into the strange metal tunnel, and this time he moved farther and farther inside the trap.

His great body blocked the door and he followed his nose to the source of those odors. Salivary juices filled his mouth. Then he reached the bait; hunger had overcome his caution.

Nick took the meat in his teeth. With a single powerful side swing of his head he tore the bait from the trigger. He heard then the sharp banging directly behind him. Forgetting the meat, he twisted and turned in the tunnel, but he was too big to turn about as the smaller bear had done. He backed as fast as he could and hit the steel door of the trap with his broad backside. His surprised "woof!" boomed so loudly that his voice resounded hollowly inside the metal trap.

Unable to turn around and unable to back out, Nick bellowed in anger and clawed at the sides of the trap, but his sharp, curving claws raked harmlessly against the steel. He roared in his rage again and again. Nick reached out for some object to tear apart and the only thing he found was the metal pipe that served as a trigger for the trap. He ripped the pipe from its anchoring but it resisted all his efforts to bite it in two.

Eventually he lay down within the dark trap, panting, frustrated, and exhausted. Gradually his nerves calmed. This was no garbage can, no car door, no canvas tent. He was accustomed to having metal, wood, and other man-made objects come apart before the power of his broad feet. But this situation was hopeless, and eventually he came to accept it.

Now he found again the pound of bait. He ate the beef, but this only sharpened his appetite. The night was a long one. With each passing hour his hunger grew.

Shortly after daylight began to dilute the blackness, Nick heard the motor. He knew the sound of automobiles. This sound was part of his world. He associated it with the people who brought him delicacies to eat along the highway. The engine stopped very close to his trap. He stood now as high as he could in the confines of his prison.

Instead of offering him food the two men came close to the door of the trap. One of them shone a brilliant white light into the darkness of the trap. Nick growled deep in his throat. Now the light dropped to his front feet. "That's him," said the man. "That's Three Toes."

The truck was hitched once more to the trailer tongue. Then it lurched forward as the trap and its trailer came up out of the holes. It moved off down the forest lane, back through the campground where the early risers were stirring, and off onto the blacktop highway.

Nick tried to sit up, but the swaying of the truck

around the curves of the mountain highway threw him to his side again. For a while he half sat, half lay there, waiting for whatever would happen next.

His trip lasted more than two hours and took him all the way to the other end of the national park. The park officials did not want Nick to go back. If by some chance he should return, trouble almost certainly lay ahead for him. One sudden angry swipe of his great claws at a park visitor or one instance of serious property damage would leave the rangers with no choice but to kill him.

The truck stopped briefly in front of a roadside restaurant, then jerked forward again. After another half hour of bumping over logging trails, the truck stopped.

One of the men sealed the ventilation holes in the back wall of the trap with strips of tape. He draped a piece of heavy canvas over the front door. Then, inside the trap Nick heard the hissing of a small spray gun and shortly he could detect a sweet smell all around him. After spraying a pound and a half of anesthetic into the trap, the man stopped and waited.

After a few minutes the two men opened the door of the trap. They fastened a rope to the rear leg of the big bear and, using a pulley attached to the trunk of a tree, dragged him from the trap onto the ground. He lay there in a limp, harmless sleep while the men trussed his four feet together tightly.

They attached the arm of a portable scales to the trunk of a tree above the animal. Then, using a block and tackle, they winched the bear off the ground until he was suspended from the arm of the scales.

After they had lowered the bear to the ground again and given him another dose of ether from a rag soaked and placed in the bottom of a bucket held over his face, they began measuring the animal with a tape measure. One of the men wrote down the figures as they were collected. "Length from tip of nose to tip of tail—64 inches. Rear paw—7¾ inches by 4 inches. Measurement from nose to back of skull—14 inches. Weight—503 pounds."

"Old Three Toes," one of the men said, "is the biggest bear I've ever seen, and I've worked in this park for eighteen years." He dipped a large paint brush into a can of yellow paint and splashed the liquid on the bear's forehead. Now Nick had become a marked bear. Anywhere in the park, the yellow mark would brand him as a bear with a record.

After they removed the ropes from Nick's feet, the men sat in the truck waiting. A few minutes later the big bear moved his head. He opened his eyes and sat up. He sat still for several minutes, then shook his head from side to side and stood up on wobbly feet. Quickly he was returning to normal. He turned and trotted unsteadily toward the nearby forest. Behind him, the two watching men hoped they had seen the last of the bear they called Three Toes.

109

Chapter
13

*T*he cool, sharp mountain air began to clear his head. The solid earth beneath his broad feet seemed to restore his sense of natural balance. He began trotting, to put distance between himself and this place. A few minutes later he broke into a gallop, and shortly he was plunging through the forest at a speed of nearly twenty-five miles an hour.

Direction seemed not to matter. Nick did not know why he ran, except that he was going away from the people who had imprisoned him and forced their will upon him.

Finally, angling up the mountainside, he slowed to a walk. He stopped, out of breath, and looked at the world around him. The oaks, hickories, beech, and maples were familiar, but the countryside had no landmarks he recognized. It resembled his home range, but not once did he see any tree, rock, or creek that he had seen before.

He walked deliberately into the most tangled laurel thickets he had ever encountered. He spent his temper on saplings and walked grudgingly around the trees he could not move.

His recent experiences in the trap, and now this strange territory, combined to sharpen his alertness. The softest sound, the slightest motion attracted his attention. The raucous call of a bluejay brought him up short, the falling of a dead twig, the scurrying of a frightened squirrel—each added to his nervous mood.

After more than an hour of wandering without plan or purpose, Nick gradually became aware of the ache in his stomach. Many hours had passed since he had eaten. His stomach growled repeatedly. The bear began to look for food and stopped frequently to sniff the air for guidance.

Always he worked his way up the slope toward the ridge. Back in the country he knew so well, he would have followed the trails of the bears, but here he found no trail where the bears traveled and this added to his nervousness.

He came shortly to a great reddish log, moist and weak with rot and returning gradually to earth by the

111

forces of nature. He stopped and sniffed its base, then with an angry sweep of his mutilated paw, he tore into the soft, rotting wood. The log fell apart before him and in doing so exposed thousands of frantic ants. They rushed now in all directions. Some grasped the white grubs with whose care they were charged.

Once he tired of eating ants and grubs and had left the colony in complete destruction, Nick wandered on toward the ridge and the fog around it toward the southwest, which in some manner beyond his understanding seemed to draw him.

Here in the high reaches of the Smokies he passed out of the northern limits of the hardwoods and entered gradually into the spruce-fir belt. At the peaks of these mountains the combination of high rainfall, thin soil, and low temperatures reproduced those North Woods conditions suited to the growth of spruce and fir. Beneath these towering giants Nick wandered through the open forest, his footsteps silenced by the thick, absorbant carpets of green, moist mosses. In this symbiotic society of ground-hugging mosses and towering evergreens, food for the bear was less abundant than in the lowlands.

But he stopped once to eat the glossy blue berries of the amber-bell that he found hanging in small clusters a few inches above the ground. And at four thousand feet above sea level he tasted briefly the tender white stems of the Indian pipe. For Nick this journey across the ridge of the mountains, more than a mile above sea level, was a new experience.

In the days that followed he wandered aimlessly.

112

He followed whatever urge he felt at the moment. Rarely did he find a tree on which bears had left their marks. Nick himself seldom knew why he turned uphill or down, why he stayed along the thickly grown up creek bottoms or the mountain ridges masked in their blue-gray haze. Yet almost from the first day of his new freedom, a strange force directed his feet southward and westward.

He was a long way, however, from his old haunts. If he had traveled directly in the straight lines of the migrating birds, he would have covered the distance in a few days. He would also have encountered other campgrounds, not the ones he knew in his old territory, but which would still have provided him food from the campers' kitchens. This might also have shortened his life considerably. The splash of yellow paint on his head was the mark of a troublemaker. He would carry the yellow mark until he shed his fur and took on a new heavy winter coat in early autumn.

Nick wandered where his search for food, his fear of danger, and his moods led him. He had no way of knowing that early one morning he crossed out of the park.

Now the bear had entered the vast timberlands of the big national forest that stretched for miles. Although he did not realize it, he had taken a turn away from his home territory.

He came one day over a ridge and down to a small creek, frothing and rushing between the rocks. Beside the creek was a narrow, twisting, hard-surfaced road. An automobile passed, but the bear stayed in the thick

113

bushes and the car did not stop. Nick could hear strange sounds ahead now and he moved more cautiously, because these were man's sounds.

His experience warned Nick away from the village. He had learned that some people fed him and some people hurt him. And he never knew which to expect.

He circled above the town. Eventually he sat on his haunches in the deep woods listening and sniffing the air rising from the village below. He wandered into a laurel thicket and slept uneasily.

Later that night he found the place to which townspeople hauled their refuse up the mountainside a short distance to dump it into the head of a gully where the red earth lay exposed and washed by the rains. He stood a few minutes above the dump, then made his way stiff-legged down the soft bank toward the tangled collection of broken furniture, tin cans, and scraps of garbage. After he had explored the dump without satisfying his appetite completely, he climbed back out of the gully and walked off toward the woods above the town. Behind him he left the broad prints of his big paws freshly pressed in the soft earth.

During the day that followed he was content to sleep and rest quietly in his bed far up the mountain. But with the coming of darkness and the renewed gnawing of hunger in his belly, he thought again of the dump. Slowly he stood and stretched and then moved off down the trail toward the village.

This time Nick came directly down the gully to the

place where it deepened and broadened and its mouth fanned out above the town. A quarter of a mile farther down the slope he could see the lights of the town, dim through the summer foliage of the trees and half hidden by a thin veil of misty fog that had settled into the valley with the coming of evening.

He nosed a large tin can to one side, and the metallic rattle filled the night with sound. As the can rolled to a stop the bear suddenly found himself blinking into two big yellow lights shining into his face from the edge of the gully above him.

Like some giant black shadow he rushed to escape, and as he moved, the bullet from a high-caliber rifle crashed into the cans beside him. The crack of the gun had hardly reached his ears before he was scrambling across the piles of trash and racing, not up the hill in the direction of the light, but down the mountain straight toward the town.

Almost before he realized what had happened he had reached the edge of the first yard. He dashed around the house and across the road in front of the row of buildings. He ran through another yard and disappeared once more into the night. In the morning the men found his great tracks through the town. They brought their hounds and put them to the trail. But they were too late, for Nick had not hesitated. He had kept moving most of that night.

Chapter 14

*A*fter resting the following day, Nick rose sleepily from his bed and pushed out to the edge of the thicket. He sat there idly for a few minutes, looking from one side to the other, sniffing the air. There was some strangeness that disturbed him.

Nick had often smelled cooking fires around the campground, and he had known the odors of burning oak rising from Swope's chimney beyond the big park. But this smoke seemed to be everywhere. It was in all the air around him.

He turned his head again to watch and to listen, and from far down the slope he could hear the crackling of the burning trees and underbrush. He could see rolling black clouds rising from the earth, and they were strangely unlike the common storm clouds that often drifted across the ridges and peaks.

For several weeks the forest service had warned of a

growing threat in the timberlands. The late summer was unusually dry, and early autumn found all the fire towers manned day and night. Anxious eyes constantly scanned distant slopes and ridges. In their growing concern the forest workers had sent warnings out around the countryside, and had reluctantly banned fires in the forest campgrounds.

In the few minutes since rising from his bed Nick had sensed a danger in this new development and he began trotting away to the north and west, away from the suffocating smoke and the crackling woodlands. Less than a mile behind him the orange flames of the forest fire pushed up the mountainside on a front ten miles wide.

To the creatures of the woods, fire is a frightening force beyond the power of the wild animal's reasoning, a force which leaves no reaction but fear, no hope but escape. Now Nick and smaller creatures as well ran before the approaching flames.

The fire burned the leaves, licked at the bark of the trees, and climbed each tree individually from the ground up. As the flames grew in intensity, the woodlands became insufferably hot. The forest fire crept up along the slopes through the home of the wild hog and into the trees where the gray squirrels lived and where the warblers had joined the vireos and woodpeckers. The fire pushed Nick, but he easily stayed well ahead of it.

He tired eventually and stopped to rest, but when he thought again of the fire, he moved on. He fed as he traveled. At last the fire seemed far behind, and when Nick came to a rocky ledge he slowed to a walk and noticed a cavern in the rocks. He stuck his sensitive nose into the black face of the opening and the air for the first time in hours felt cool and moist to him, and free of the smell of smoke. He pushed deeper into the cavern, and lay down to rest.

While the bear slept, the fire advanced. The wind came on steadily out of the southeast. Foresters and farmers had gathered to cope with the leaping flames, but the fire had become a wall before the driving wind. It gnawed its way through the mountains, driving away or burning everything in its path.

Toward midnight the fire approached the shelf of rock where the bear slept. Suddenly his dreams of the fire had become real. He rose to his feet and walked to the mouth of the cave. Arms of the fire had moved around his position like great pincers. Already the jaws of the pincers had passed both ends of the cliff. And there, a quarter of a mile in front of Nick's cave, was the frightening wall of flames. There was no escape.

Nick stood undecided for a few minutes. He tried climbing over the edge of the cliff toward the top, but loose stones tumbled him to the bottom again. Nick arose and looked again at the approaching flames. He growled and then, in sudden fear, he whimpered as he had not done since he was a yearling cub.

His only path of escape lay behind him, not over the cliff but back into the cave. He sat in his bed nervously listening to the crackling of the flames and the whine of the rising hot wind. The red glow was reflected on the wall opposite him, and the air inside his cave became steadily warmer. The bear pushed as far to the rear of the cave as he could squeeze, and without hesitating forced his bulk into a crevice between two long, jagged black rocks.

He could do no more. His nose lay close against the cave floor. He waited and panted in the heat. When the smoke from the burning wood became stronger than ever, he lay coughing and gasping on the floor of the cave, unable any longer to struggle or fight.

Had the fire burned on much longer around the front of the rock ledge, Nick would have died there, far from his birthplace. He would have died like the foxes, deer, skunk, wild hogs, and ruffed grouse caught without protection on the slopes below. But the fire moved on and left the black land it had devastated, in mourning. Nick gradually became aware of cooler air filtering into the cave. Later the pain in his starved lungs subsided, but for hours he stayed inside the cave.

Some time late in the night Nick heard the noise in the sky. For many weeks he had not heard it. Thunder sounded through the mountains. Out of the southeast, lightning flashed over the smoldering ruins of great trees. Rain began to fall.

At last Nick stood up stiffly in the cave. Slowly he padded out and picked his way gingerly between blackened logs, still smoking in spite of the drenching rain

119

of the night before. He could see for great distances through the burned-over woodlands. No longer were there abundant places to hide, and this filled him with wonder. But shortly his attention was caught by the discovery of the blackened carcasses of a doe and her yearling fawn. Bears seldom will attack a full-grown deer, but they are carrion eaters. Before moving on, Nick ate all he could hold of the venison.

A few hours later he came to the end of the burned-out area. Here the storm had caught up with the fire. He was once more in woodland surroundings.

In the days that had passed since he left the sanctuary of the national park, Nick had wandered farther and farther from his home territory. Now he was many miles from the nearest border of the park. But one day he came to a mountain gap and stopped as if wondering about the course he should follow. Then he began picking his way down the far side into still another great valley where he had never been before.

Chapter
15

In the last half of a dark night Nick came out of the woods to a place where a narrow blacktop road wound through the forest. For some time he walked uphill along the road. Around him now the night was black and quiet, but he detected the faint smell of wood smoke mingled with food odors.

Rounding the bend in the little road, he came to a long, low log structure. Years ago this famous lodge had been built here among the giant trees. Its patrons had come from distant cities—Cincinnati, Pittsburgh, and Chicago. They had come in summer to swim and ride and relax in the wilderness setting, in later years they came in winter too, bringing their heavy clothing and their skis. But this was a season between, the time of the fall colors, and the Smoky Mountains are famous far and wide for the brilliance and variety of their autumn foliage. People had flocked in until every room was filled with weekend guests.

Hours earlier the Saturday night dance had ended and the band had departed. The weary vacationers were deep in slumber. To Nick, standing in the front yard looking speculatively at the lodge, it seemed that perhaps he was the only one awake. He lifted himself up the half-dozen steps to the long porch along the front of the lodge. He walked the length of the porch, swinging to right and left, stopping occasionally to investigate. At the end of the porch, instead of turning and retracing his steps, he chose to climb up on the railing. Minutes later he was on the roof of the porch. From this position it was not difficult for him to scramble to the higher level of the lodge roof. He padded quietly along the roof of the lodge until he came to that part of it that covered the great central lobby.

Nick came upon the skylight from its upper edge. While bracing himself to keep from sliding down the roof he tentatively put out one forepaw and tested this strange surface. It resembled very much the thin sheet of ice which he had occasionally discovered across the mountain brooks. With exploratory pressure he pushed gently on the glass and, surprisingly, it suddenly broke beneath the weight of his heavy foot. Thrown suddenly off balance, Nick was propelled forward.

In the next instant the startled bear found himself falling through space. Fortunately perhaps for Nick, he thudded into the padded surface of a long leather couch.

It cracked and tilted forward and Nick rolled off onto the floor. For almost a minute he sat on the bearskin rug before the couch.

He looked around him with mixed emotions. Until this moment, at least, no humans had come to challenge him, but their odor hung heavy in the room. There were other smells too, and Nick followed his nose to the big kitchen. Inside the door just to his left he found a large can of flour. The lid came off easily. He tipped it over. The barrel rolled the length of the room and a layer of white dust was left in its wake. Nick's attention turned to the food spread on the work table in preparation for breakfast. He stood up to the table and, using one forearm as a push broom, swept the surface clear of bread, breakfast rolls and assorted glassware, all of which mixed with the flour on the floor.

He stopped briefly to eat one package of sweet rolls, and then rose to investigate a new attraction. He had come to the heavy door of the cold-storage room. He found that the handle on the edge of the door moved downward beneath the pressure of his paw, and the door swung open. Nick dropped to all four feet, and stuck his head into the cold room, which was lighted by a single electric bulb that turned on automatically when the door opened. The sights and smells spread before him were enough to delight any raiding black bear. He found first a bushel of juicy red apples and tipped the basket on its side so that they rolled across the floor in a delightful display before him. Stuck back beneath a row of shelves

123

was a square wooden crate. He dragged the crate from beneath the shelves and in so doing tipped it onto one side. Dozens of white eggs rolled from the crate and mixed with the red apples. Nick picked up one of the eggs and with the yellow yolk dripping from the corners of his mouth made his way across the floor of the pantry.

Resting on blocks against the rear wall of the pantry was a large wooden barrel. A spigot projected from the barrel. The bear grasped it in his teeth, and wrenched the plug from the cask. Suddenly there was a sound like the gurgling of a mountain brook, as riffles of fresh cider washed across the floor to combine with the broken eggs and rolling red apples.

When Nick attempted to cross the room he found it difficult to maintain his footing. He slipped, landed on his haunches, and found himself sliding with startling speed toward the far corner of the little room.

In a frantic effort to stop himself he reached out and grasped the framework supporting the rows of shelves lining one side of the cold room, and hung on. Shelves, large cans, glasses, crocks, pans, quarters of beef, and bottle upon bottle of milk showered around and over the startled bear. For some minutes he simply sat in the midst of this strange mixture and waited.

That Nick had proceeded as far and as long as he had without human detection was incredible. It is true that the heavily insulated walls of the cold room muffled much of the noise. But now the cook's alarm clock went off in a room downstairs in the lodge. The cook got

dressed, came from his room, and walked along the carpeted hall toward the main dining area. With growing disbelief he looked around him. Scattered across the floor of the lobby was a blanket of broken glass. And the couch seemed strangly bent in the middle. Now the man looked above him and saw the stars shining with unusual brilliance in the black predawn sky.

The sight that greeted him when he switched on the kitchen light made him blink and shake his head in disbelief. He turned and, momentarily forgetting the comfort of the sleeping guests, yelled as loudly as he could to the assistant cook, who had not yet come from his room. "Lord Amighty, LeRoy," he called, "get on down here. Some bear's tore literal hell out of the place." By the time LeRoy arrived minutes later, a few startled guests had begun to appear. First came an elderly couple who had traveled the night before all the way from Pittsburgh for a few days of peace and quiet in their favorite lodge. They shuffled down the hallway to look in speculatively through the kitchen door. Then the word spread rapidly. People who had dressed hastily, as well as many still in their dressing robes, came from the guest rooms. They crowded around the open door of the kitchen.

Before long someone asked the obvious question: where had the bear gone? The assembled people looked first at each other, then at the cook, then began casting uneasy glances into the dark recesses of the big lodge.

At this moment Nick, inside the cold room, chose to stand up amid the rubble. Objects rolled, broke, and

126

clattered, and the muffled sounds reached the people assembled outside in the kitchen.

Someone, meanwhile, had run outside to the manager's cottage. He arrived in such haste that when he entered the lodge he failed to close the large front doors behind him. The manager sized up the situation immediately. His experience in the mountains had taught him great respect for the destructive power of bears. He began at once to issue instructions and suggestions both to his cook and his guests. There was general agreement that they had the culprit trapped inside the narrow confines of the cold-storage room. The assistant cook was dispatched to the manager's cottage to get his rifle. One guest was asked to telephone the conservation officer and request that gentleman to come to the lodge as quickly as he could. It was suggested that the other guests take their leave of the kitchen and retire at least to the main room of the lodge.

At this moment Nick decided to get out of the cold room. Standing precariously on his hind legs he explored carefully the edges of the door frame. Then he discovered the round knob designed to release the latch from the inside. With an exploratory motion he pushed against it with his paw.

Many of the guests had not had time to get out of the kitchen. As the heavy door of the cold room swung open, all eyes turned in that direction. Flowing out onto the kitchen floor was a shallow stream of brown cider and white milk in which floated bobbing apples and broken egg shells. In the middle of this gentle flood stood a very large bear. Half of him was black as usual, half was white with flour. Nick stood with his head and shoulders projecting from the open door. He moved his head first to one side then the other, surveying the scene before him. And as he moved into the kitchen, people scrambled madly to get out of the room.

Suddenly Nick made a rush for the open door of the big room, and the cook, leaping from his path, slipped and fell into the flour. The cook, also covered now with a film of white dust, grabbed a broom and began swatting Nick across his broad rump. The bear halted, turned, and swung one paw with a force that sent the broom hurtling across the dining room.

The cook hastily withdrew and joined the ring of people around the wall of the big room. In search of an avenue of escape, Nick ran first in one direction then another while yelling men and screaming women pushed to get out of his path. The now well-lighted long halls of the lodge stretching off in either direction seemed the only logical paths left open to him. He bolted at full speed along the carpeted floor and in a matter of seconds had reached the end of the hallway. With his path blocked, he turned and saw before him an empty guest room where the lights burned and the door stood open.

Nick permitted himself time enough to sweep the top of the dresser clear of all the items that littered it. He walked over the bed and felt it sag to the floor beneath his weight. He slashed open a pillow and a cloud of feathers rose and drifted about him. Then he left the room and ran back along the hall.

Now he turned and galloped into the big room again. He stood undecided in the middle of the floor, moving his head first in one direction then the other, while the ring of spectators crowded against the wall away from him. At this moment the headlights of an approaching vehicle swung around the last curve in the road, and their flashing beams came through the open front door directly into the eyes of the bear. He saw an escape route he had not seen before and ran out through the big front door.

Nick leaped from the porch and as he did so the doors of the vehicle opened. Nick turned to his left, running as fast as possible, and he was soon swallowed up in the black shadows of the thick vegetation. Behind him he left, in addition to the mess, an expert marksman who had lacked sufficient time and light even to find the bear in the sights of his gun.

During the following weeks Nick concentrated on feeding and storing fat that would sustain him through the approaching winter. And as cold weather caught up with him, he was still wandering through territory he had never seen before.

Chapter
16

*I*n the approaching darkness of an evening during the following summer, Nick passed through a gap at Harper Mountain and stood for a brief time in bold silhouette on an outcropping of rock. From this spot he could look down on the scene spread below him in the valley. Dim yellow lights had begun to mark the movement of people there. The bear's mind turned to the food these people would have with them. He directed his footsteps down the mountain and toward the settlement.

Later, when Jeremy Hillards closed his combination service station-grocery store for the night, Nick was still working his way to the bottom of the mountain. He seemed in no hurry. He turned over logs as he came to them and paused often to sniff the night air for clues to food.

In the middle of the night he stood secluded in the

brush across from Hillards' store. His head protruded from the thicket as he searched the scene for signs of danger. Nowhere did a person move or a dog bark. Only rarely did the lights of a speeding automobile pass in the night. Nick waded through the shallow creek, climbed the embankment, and crossed the highway. He stayed hidden in the shadows of the store and the trees.

He plodded around the buildings and came again to the north side. Here he lifted his nose high, and detected at once the heavy smell of foods in the air. He traced the direction with his nose, and began to follow the invisible trail. It led him straight to a large wire cage.

At Nick's approach, a small black cub lifted its head a few inches from the floor of its cage. He stared in fright at the great black animal visible in the pale light of the one yellow bulb above the station door. The cub whimpered and scooted to the far side of the cage. Nick, however, seemed to ignore the smaller bear; he walked around the outside of the cage sniffing carefully as he came. When he came close to the side of the cage where the cub lay, the little bear rose weakly on his wobbly legs and backed to the opposite side of the pen. The cub's fur was shaggy and unkempt, and his eyes had a dull look.

In the three months the bear had been held prisoner he had grown steadily more listless. In recent days he had refused even to eat. Around him at this moment in the cage were leftover meat and vegetables from the Hil-

131

lards' dinner table. "I feed that thing well enough," Hillards had told his wife. "I give it fruit, vegetables, meat, dog food, and stuff from the table. I'll tell you what I think; I think he sold me a sick bear. And I think I ought to get my three hundred dollars back. That mangy-looking little critter won't bring me three hundred dollars' return in forty years the way he mopes around all the time."

Not once had Hillards ever questioned his right to keep a bear in a cage. "One thing people come to these hills to see is the bears," he would say. "They come along this highway heading for the park and this is one of the first bears they get to see. I'm doing them a favor, having a bear here where they can see it easy and safe. And it helps business."

Now in the middle of the night, Hillards was asleep on the second floor of his store. Outside, where people stopped and looked each day at this scraggly cub, there stood the biggest and finest of black bears anywhere in the Great Smokies.

Concerned as he was with the nearness of the food, Nick had forgotten some of his native caution. He stood up and tested the door. The food inside was almost within his reach. He hooked the powerful claws of his front foot through the wire of the door. With a mighty heave of his shoulders he rattled the door on its hinges until the entire cage shook and trembled like the limbs of an apple tree.

He might have demolished the cage and brought it

crashing to the ground except for the fact that suddenly the latch on the door came loose. The creaking door swung half way open and the bear dropped again to all four feet while the door swayed gently back and forth. Nick hit it viciously with his paw and slammed it open so hard that it clattered back against the screened side of the cage. The sudden noise startled the big bear and now he stopped and looked around. But he saw no other creatures in the night except for the small cub quaking in the corner of the cage. Then, one slow step at a time, Nick went into the cage, sniffing in exploration as he advanced.

As Nick entered, the cub scooted sideways around him and bolted out of the enclosure into the night. Nick made a halfhearted swat at the tiny black form as it passed him, but missed the cub. He went to the food.

The lure of the meat had become so strong that Nick did not even notice the stealthy approach of an enemy. Hillards, awakened by Nick's rattling of the cage, had crawled sleepily from his bed. Leaning on his window sill he stared in disbelief at the drama being enacted in the dim light below. "Must be a wild one," he thought. "Nobody along this road has a bear that big."

The fascinated store owner was frozen there in inactivity until it suddenly dawned on him that this great black bear, standing taller than a man, might actually break into his bear cage and kill his cub. Then Hillards, triggered into action, scurried downstairs in the dark. He grabbed his shotgun from the corner of the back room and filled the chambers with shells loaded with buck-shot. He opened the door as quietly as he was able, and silently cursed his failure to oil the creaking hinges.

He sneaked along the side of his store, hiding in the shadows, taking each step cautiously to keep from stumbling over objects lying in the yard.

When Hillards came to the corner of the station, he stopped. He wondered for a moment if the wild events of the last few minutes had really happened. Then, with a sinking feeling, he realized that the door of his bear cage was swinging open. The big bear was actually going in-side the cage. And there went his cub hell-bent for the sticks. He had shown more signs of life in these few minutes than Hillards had seen him display in all the weeks before. The man checked his impulse to pursue the animal. Already a better plan was taking shape in Hillards' mind.

Very quietly he began creeping toward the cage. He noted that the wind was in his favor, and he stayed close to the shadows. Now he could see the bear better. The animal seemed almost to fill the cage! What a prize this would be. Nick stopped once in his eating and held his head high to sniff the night air, then turned his attention back to the food.

As he approached the cage, Hillards picked up an oak plank. The sudden clatter of the heavy door slam-ming shut brought Nick wheeling about so fast that for a fraction of a second Hillards considered dropping his insane scheme and dashing for the refuge of his house.

But his hands worked faster than his mind and carried out his plan. As the door slammed shut, the plank went into place against it, and Hillards rammed the other end of the plank into the soft earth to brace the door. In an instant, the big bear had traded places with a sickly cub that now ran free in the woods.

Hillards quickly brought another plank to brace the door. Inside the cage the big bear was running from one wall to the other grunting in rage, striking the bars, and looking for an opening. Hillards, grinning in wonder at the deed he had performed, and considerably frightened by the bear he had imprisoned, backed slowly toward his house.

With a savage snarl Nick rushed against the heavy wire bars that trapped him. The side of the cage bent before his weight, but the heavy wire bounced him back in a heap onto the floor. He stood up and struck the wire repeatedly in his wild fury but could neither slash it nor tear it loose. For the moment, the cage held against his onslaught. The man backed away and entered the building. Nick sat glumly in the middle of the cage.

For many minutes he looked around him at the infuriating enclosure. This man had robbed him of his freedom to roam the mountainsides as he chose and to be alone, as was his nature. In the following minutes the bear's mood grew as black as his coat. There, reaching to the distant sky beyond the highway, was the dark form of the beckoning mountain.

In Nick's experience there was but one part of this

cage that opened. He had come in by the door. He had opened it by shaking it. He stood now high on his hind feet and gripped the heavy wire of the cage door at the level of his powerful shoulders. Maddened, he shook the door with growing vigor. He shook it harder than he had ever shaken anything before, and continued to shake it until the wire box rattled and trembled as if tossed by an earthquake. The corner posts of the cage were weaving back and forth like paw-paw trees in an April storm, and the whole frame creaked and cracked.

Meanwhile Hillards, who had returned to his bed, heard this renewed commotion. He vaulted up, and in his haste stumbled into a bedside chair that clattered to the floor of the darkened room. He leaned on the window sill and for the second time this night stared in speechless disbelief. "That fool bear," he thought, "will tear his cage apart shaking it that way."

Without bothering this time to pull his pants on over his nightshirt, the store owner half ran, half fell down the flight of stairs and into the back room of the store. He groped for the light cord, grabbed his shotgun, and ran out with the tail of his night clothes billowing behind him.

At the very moment that he dashed madly from the side door, Hillards saw Nick bring the entire cage crashing over on its side, and the great bear dashed away toward the peaceful, forested mountains from which he had wandered such a short time before.

In the dust to his left a charge of buckshot rattled.

136

But Hillards was so unnerved by now that he could not have hit the side of a barn from the inside. And as Nick raced to the safety of the mountains, he left behind a man who stood almost sobbing in his driveway.

The next day and for many days thereafter, Hillards would point to his demolished bear cage and tell the story. It lost nothing in the telling. And it became a legend, a legend of a great devil-bear that came down from the mountains and set captive bears free.

Chapter
17

Some weeks later Nick's travels brought him to the community of Moses Corners. Here, many miles from the national park, bears were neither so common nor so bold as they were in the area where Nick was born. There were a few in the forests, but years had passed since anyone had seen a wild bear in the community of Moses Corners itself.

Before he reached the outer limits of the settlement Nick came upon a small field fenced with three strands of barbed wire, where Sterling Beauchamp pastured half a dozen head of yearling calves. The bear stood looking at the calves as they moved around in the semidarkness. Long hours had passed since he had eaten substantially, and his hunger had mounted steadily. As he crouched and pushed against the lowest wire, it gave way, and he struggled beneath the fence. The calves, seeing this huge black apparition among them, panicked. They scattered and one of the smaller ones bounced against the wire, wheeled, and ran back directly toward the big bear.

Nick had never before killed a calf. Most black bears are not stock killers, but those that do learn to kill domestic animals are most often large male bears. If Nick had no intention of killing one of the animals, he changed his mind in this final moment. It seemed to him that the frenzied animal would run him down, and he reared up on his hind feet just as the calf recovered its sense of direction and wheeled to miss the bear. The change of direction came too late. With a swing of his front paw Nick clouted the bawling calf in the side of the head.

The calf's head snapped to the side as if it were hinged, and the animal rolled over several times and then lay kicking in the grass. No more sounds came from the calf and soon it lay perfectly still. Nick sniffed it then grasped its neck in his jaws and began backing with it toward the woods. The fence stopped him and because he saw no reason to fear for his own safety, he stayed there to eat part of the calf.

If Nick had left the community of Moses Corners at that time, the monster stories might have died down faster. Nick traveled in a great circle and for most of a week stayed within eight miles of the settlement, while tales of his escapades spread with startling swiftness.

One farmer told of his hounds. He had heard them howling in the night. "It wasn't like dogs howling at the moon. It was more like howling at the sight of death.

And in the morning, the hounds were cowering and whimpering and would not leave the back door of the house. I've never seen them act like they acted this morning," their owner said.

One of his neighbors reported seeing a great shaggy beast disappear suddenly in front of his headlights as he rounded a curve. On the other side of the little settlement a flock of six domestic turkeys was destroyed and a shoat was killed. After these strange events, children were kept indoors and chickens and livestock were caught up and locked in barns and pens each evening.

A threat to family and property can go just so long. Then man rises in defense of his own. Petty personal differences are put aside. A plan must be worked out. So on these first cool nights of early autumn Nick continued to move about the countryside fattening himself on whatever he could find to eat, while a great campaign was being mounted against him.

More than thirty men and boys gathered at Plover Grade School one evening. They came jolting down from the hollows in pickup trucks and sedans, and they drove in from the settlements around the countryside. They congregated for a single purpose—to organize the biggest monster hunt these hills had ever seen.

How many hounds did they need? All they could get! They took a count and figured they might have fifty or sixty. And almost everybody had a gun and intended to bring it. The hunt was set for eight o'clock the next morning, which would give time to get the chores done.

They would meet here at the school and try to get the hounds to pick up a trail. From then on there was no telling what might happen.

But one farmer, Bucky Ellison, just plain did not believe in monsters. "Look at it this way," he had explained to his wife one morning at the breakfast table, "if it's not a bear, what is it?"

"That's what I'd like to know," she said quietly.

"Men have lived in these hills two hundred and fifty years," Bucky insisted. "I can't believe there are wild beasts here people never saw. Exceptin' those that get their start in a bottle."

Bucky had a reputation up and down the valley for being friendly with everyone, but independent too, and sometimes seeming to argue just to keep the talk going. It was also known that Bucky was not above pulling a practical joke. Now a masterful plot took shape in Bucky's mind. A devilish grin spread slowly across his features.

Later that night he found a piece of plywood and cut from it a section eight inches across and fifteen inches long. Then he sawed it until it became rounded on the front and had a big toe sticking out on the left side. Then he nailed on some pieces of rubber hose to pad it. There was only one additional feature needed.

From the cupboard off the hallway he took a pair of old shoes he hadn't worn for years. He threw the left one into the trash can and nailed the other one solidly on top of the wooden paw.

141

Nick, meanwhile, had turned to his favorite diet of berries and nuts. Acorns were falling from the trees. Pawpaws and persimmons were ripe. The tasty rich nuts of the beech trees were there for the taking.

Late that night he crossed the creek and made his way up the timbered slope beyond. He was drowsy and soon he stopped, sniffed, and lay down in the thick-growing underbrush for a nap.

Bucky Ellison was out of bed forty-five minutes ahead of daylight. He went to his workshop and got the wooden paw from under a bushel basket where it was hidden. He stuck it in a gunny sack and climbed into his pickup truck. His wife wouldn't think anything about the truck's going out so early as sometimes he took the truck and went to the back field to get the cows started in first thing in the morning.

But this time he turned down the country road, crossed the bridge, and drove off the road into the weeds where nobody would see his truck. He climbed down to the creek, walking where the catfishermen walked, and waded into the water.

In the shallow water on the other side he put on the shoe he had nailed on the wooden paw. Now standing with his left foot in the water he set his right foot out in the soft mud on the creek bank. He lifted himself enough to put his weight on the wooden paw. Then he waded ten feet up the creek and made another print.

For nearly a quarter of a mile he continued along the creek, and occasionally set out his right foot to leave its great print in the mud. Finally, in the mud on the other side of the creek, he made a single footprint pointing toward the woods to the west. He had no way of knowing that he was only fifty yards from the trail Nick had followed two hours earlier.

By eight o'clock there were pickup trucks all around Plover School. Men and boys had brought most of the able-bodied coon, bear, and fox hounds from miles around. There were blueticks, Goodmans, Triggs, black and tans, Plotts hounds, and mountain curs. They strained at the leashes and snarled at each other while their owners, all carrying rifles and shotguns, tried to keep their hounds from fighting.

The county game warden was there, and so were two deputy sheriffs. The game warden suggested they divide the dogs and men into two groups. "Then," he said, "you can both start at the bridge and one bunch can work down the creek and the other bunch up. Sooner or later some of the dogs should cut the critter's tracks. Then everybody can get in on the trailin'." Bucky Ellison maneuvered himself into the upstream group. Somehow he figured it might be better if he wasn't in the group that discovered the monster tracks.

Five minutes later the crowd of men starting downstream gathered in awed silence around the first monster footprint Bucky had left in the mud. A runner was sent to bring the other group back so all the hounds could be put on this track. "It's more than twice as big as any bear track ever seen in these hills," someone said, "and it doesn't rightly look like a bear either." Nobody answered. They simply started working very carefully downstream in the direction the print pointed. They advanced with extreme caution now, and as quietly as their eager hounds would allow.

They found more tracks of the creature and eventually came to the monster track pointing away from the creek and toward the woods. Here the hounds were turned free and the little army of men splashed from the creek fully expecting their dogs to pick up the strange trail. At first the dogs seemed confused, but in a matter of minutes one of the lead dogs discovered Nick's trail. The hound let out a long wailing cry and headed for the woods. The others fell in behind him tumbling and shoving to get at the trail.

Far up on the mountain Nick lifted his head to listen. There were more hounds down there than he had ever before heard in one pack. He was out of bed and moving. He ran through strange territory where he had never before been. When he came upon a rocky cliff too steep for him to scale, he veered to the left and raced along the foot of the cliff. But the hounds gained on him.

Two miles from the place he had started, Nick found a second rock cliff looming on his other side. The little creek valley was enclosed. This made him uneasy. The walls of the cliffs seemed to push in upon him. He wanted to reach open spaces, to be free of the canyon. But behind him the hounds left no escape.

Then he reached the head of the valley. In front he saw that the two cliffs joined where water trickled over a face of sheer rock above. Panic came over the bear. Nick's fear quickly changed to anger. He made a leap to try to scale the face of the cliff, but it was hopeless and he slid back in the mud. He turned to face the hounds. Now he almost welcomed the approaching fight.

There were three hounds in the vanguard, and they rushed at the big bear without caution. With one slash of a front paw, Nick caught the first hound so fast that the dog was left no time for retreat. The hound already lay dying as Nick made his swipe at the second of the rangy, wailing hounds. Now the bear turned his slashing paws on the third hound, but that dog had seen enough. He reared backward and pivoted in his tracks to escape. Then even faster than he had run into the canyon, he ran out again, yapping as though death stalked him.

Now Nick saw the tree standing close to the face of the cliff. He ran to it and climbed, working his way around and around the trunk. He climbed until he was above the top of the ledge, then started walking out on a limb. His weight bent the limb toward the ground but still several feet of space separated him from the cliff top. He leaped, thumped against the earth, and scrambled to his feet above the very lip of the cliff.

He was gone before the main body of hounds arrived. The first hunters to reach the falls a few minutes later found only a wailing, frustrated pack milling around two dead hounds at the base of a sheer cliff.

"Looks as if I've got more of a mystery than I figured on," Bucky thought to himself.

All that day Nick traveled hard. He alternately trotted and galloped and was always alert for the baying of the hounds behind him.

The dogs had found his trail on the tree at the base of the cliff. And a long time later their owners had worked them around to the top of the cliff and here a few of the hounds once more picked up the big bear's scent. But by the time they set off again in mad and noisy pursuit, Nick had put a great length of the timberlands between himself and the hounds.

He came to the bank of a river and without hesitation plunged into the water. This was not one of the little trout streams he was accustomed to in the park, but a river that ran wider and deeper than any he had ever before encountered. Weary now from the running, the bear paddled downstream, permitting the current to do the work. He swam with most of his body submerged and angled gradually toward the far bank of the river.

But before coming out on the riverbank again, Nick had traveled downstream with the current for almost a mile. As he pulled his weary body onto the rocky bank he heard again, far up the river, the sound of the dogs. He trotted into the depths of the forest and kept running until he could hear them no longer.

Chapter
18

*N*ick *seemed not to hurry as he moved on from one* feeding place to the next. He detoured occasionally from his course but seldom for more than a few days at a time. Sometimes he followed trails used by other bears. There were occasional odors of strange bears and often there were the odors of hounds.

The trail led him one morning to a small fir tree where other bears had bitten and scratched their marks. Of all the bears that passed this way, none left his mark higher than Nick's. Standing to his full height Nick bit into the tree five inches higher than any other mark. With the underside of his chin he rubbed the marks of the other bears.

An hour after daylight he forced his heavy body under the branches of a windfall oak and bedded down. He slept for several hours, but toward the middle of the day he suddenly sat up in his bed. In the woods above him heavy feet now crunched leaves and twigs and sent vibrations along the forest floor.

As the sounds came closer, Nick sensed the unmistakable smell of man. With practiced stealth, he eased his bulk from the bed. His thick, soft fur made only whispering sounds as he pushed through the leaves into the open woods on the far side of the downfall.

He did not run at once. Like a great black ghost, he picked his path from shadow to shadow. Soon he moved behind a fern-covered rock that shielded him from the approaching hunter, and then he quickly left the area, running with his mouth open and his tongue hanging out. Then he listened and smelled the forest air. He was once more alone.

He continued to travel in a leisurely way through the woods until he came to a small cabin standing in the deep shadow of the giant trees. Nick stopped and studied the scene. Smoke rose from the chimney in a thin blue line. The man odors were strong, but there were no sounds to warn the bear away and there was no motion to attract his eye. The smell of the smoke made Nick ill at ease, but mingled with the fire smell were others that he recognized from his campground experiences of the past. Strong among them was that of bacon, which came, rich and tantalizing, to his sensitive nose. He moved cautiously toward the cabin door, his senses alert for the slightest warning. Several times between the edge of the woods and the door of the hunter's cabin he stopped and looked around and tested the air for new smells.

Nick pushed against the door and tried its strength. His claws could reach even higher than the door, but he found no spaces where they could hook beneath the edges of the boards. Nick dropped to all four feet and circled the cabin, searching for an entrance. He looked above him at the shuttered window in the front of the cabin, then stood up to investigate. He slapped the window with one huge paw and the clatter of the shutters banging against the frame resounded through the forest like the crack of a rifle. Startled by the noise he had created, Nick dropped to all four feet again and stood looking around nervously. He regained his composure, and shortly rose once more to investigate the window.

Along the top of the shutter was a space scarcely large enough for Nick to get a grip with the claws of his foot. He tugged on the shutters. On the next try, however, he forced the shutters far enough open to secure his grip on the back of the wooden panels.

In his arms and shoulders he had strength enough to break the neck of a pony or yearling steer with a single blow, and with this strength he ripped the wood in one great angry sweeping motion. One of the shutters came off as the hinges were ripped from their moorings in the log frame, and the other one fell into kindling wood at his feet. Then with a smack of his right front paw he sent the glass showering across the cabin floor.

Through the open window came a flood of interesting odors. Nick turned and surveyed the clearing around the cabin once more and then hoisted his great bulk to the sill and squeezed through the opening. A tin can of jam drew his attention. He grabbed it, dug his claws into the metal, and shook the can. The jam flew out on the floor and Nick lapped it greedily. He took a few slices of fresh bread from the wrapper but lost interest when he saw the slab of bacon hanging from a rafter out of reach. He tried standing to his full height to reach the bacon, but it was still too high for him. This enraged Nick, and he looked around the cabin angrily for other items on which to feed or vent his anger. He found both. Breakfast cereals were opened and strewn about. A sack of flour was slashed and emptied, a bag of sugar yielded its contents to the growing heap of rubble.

He swept the dishes and pans from the plank table then promptly tore the door from the ice chest. Out came the eggs and butter as well as steaks, intended for the hunters' evening meal. This treasure momentarily took his mind off everything else. He ate eggs, smeared butter over his face, and consumed the steaks.

Then he remembered the wonderful smell which had first attracted his attention. He propped his front paws on the edge of the table and sniffed the bacon above him repeatedly. Then he lifted one of his hind feet to the edge of the table. With a grunt he heaved himself up.

Before he could rise to his feet and grab the prize dangling above his head, the table tottered and leaned crazily farther and farther toward one side. It crashed with a resounding clatter, dumping Nick in the midst of the debris he had scattered on the floor. Startled now by the noise, and amply fed, he forced his way out again through the window and trotted off into the forest.

On this day early in the new hunting season the woods were filled with hazards. At least twice before darkness came he would have this impressed upon him.

A hunter can seldom sneak up on a bear in the woods. The bear's hearing warns him far in advance of the man's approach. But sometimes it is the other way around. If the hunter is quiet and hidden and the wind does not carry his scent toward the bear, the animal may come upon the hunter before either of them realizes it.

Nick had traveled a little more than a mile along the ridge since visiting the cabin. At the time Nick had called on them, the bow hunters were hidden out on the mountain, waiting at deer crossings for game to come past their stands. From the corner of his eye one of them caught the motion of a big bear swinging down the old logging road. He turned very slowly for a better look at the creature and got a good look at the bear's huge bulk. He gripped the bow in an effort to keep his hand from shaking with excitement.

Nick padded on and the yards between him and the bow hunter diminished rapidly—eighty, seventy, sixty, fifty; the bow was being drawn to its full power now. The razor sharp broadhead on the arrow was being lined up on the bear's chest.

Then, scarcely thirty yards from the hunter, Nick sensed the man's presence. With an explosive woof the big bear heaved himself from the trail, veered sharply to the left, and lumbered off through the woods. Behind him, the hunting arrow whirred and slid harmlessly beneath the leaves. Nick ran for more than four miles before slowing down.

Late in the day he lifted his head to test the air for some rich and promising smell the soft wind had carried to him through the trees. He sniffed several times, then began walking with cautious steps into the wind.

He traveled more than half a mile and the odor was growing steadily stronger. Now the bear, made nervous and alert by recent events, stopped frequently to sniff and search the woods about him for strange sights and sounds. Two hundred yards away, and still partly screened by the thick-growing brush, a man crouched motionless beside the base of a huge maple tree, his .30/06 rifle resting across his knees. He did not move, but watched every movement of the big bear.

If the man had his calculations right, the path of the bear would bring it within fifty yards of his stand—if, of course, the bear took a direct path to the bait. But sometimes you can figure everything just right, then have it go wrong at the last minute. He had dragged the fresh beef head through the woods in a gunny sack and set it up on a stump where bears should smell it if they had any nose at all. And now this big fellow looked as though he was just about to come to his last bait.

But before Nick came around the screen of brush and into range of the rifle, the whispering of the wind increased in intensity. Both the hunter and the bear sensed the shifting of the wind. "Damn infernal luck," the hunter whispered, and even as he said it, Nick be-

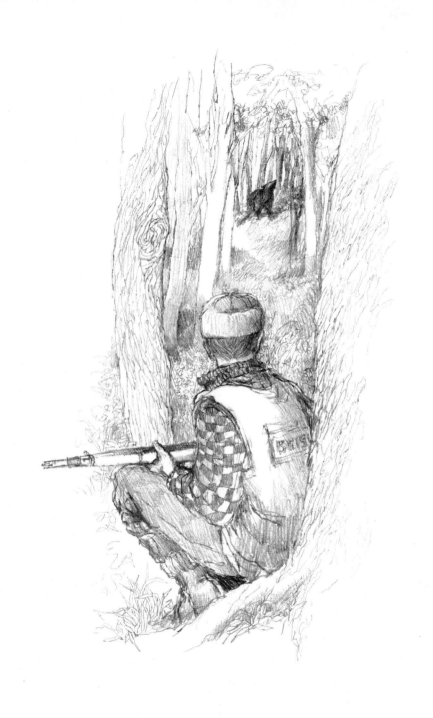

came aware that the odors of the meat were mixed with those of man in this forest where men meant danger.

As Nick whirled and changed his course, he felt a single searing flash of pain across the top of his shoulders. He heard the shot as the impact rolled him from his feet. He heard another shot but felt no more bullets, and now he was up and running. The bullet had only cut through the thick fat layer over his shoulders.

Twice in a single day he left frustrated hunters far behind, but instead of elation, Nick felt only a continuing sense of apprehension.

Eventually, long after darkness came, he slept. Later in the night he awakened and moved on until he found a hillside with a fine stand of beech trees where he stopped to feed. At dawn a flock of eight wild turkeys walked gingerly to the edge of the woods and began eating beechnuts. The great birds were a hundred yards from the big bear and they watched him warily.

The shoulder injury made Nick ill-tempered. He charged the turkeys, but had covered only a few yards before the large birds flew into the trees as if on signal.

The new day dawned with dark layers of fast-moving clouds hiding the distant peaks and ridges, casting the mountains into a depressing half light. Bitter winds stirred the brittle brown leaves still clinging to the oaks and beeches. Occasional flurries of snow brushed against the bear and melted quickly on his shiny black fur. In the changing season, Nick left the place, crossed Bee Sting Creek, and traveled toward the distant ridge dominated by the outline of Briartop Mountain.

Chapter
19

Luther Swope and John finished their chores early, and then, by the late light of the dull November day, proceeded to load the pickup truck. First they put in a large wooden box Luther had made to cover the truck bed, and then John brought an armload of straw to provide a bed for the dogs. Next he led out the three Plotts hounds and the half airedale. The dogs leaped eagerly into the darkness of the box and whined nervously while John and his father fastened their chains to hooks inside the traveling dog shelter.

John and Luther wore their heaviest winter clothing and carried their rifles, knives, and big flashlights. While they worked, the gray light of day disappeared and left behind a night as black as a bear's coat. The little truck moved slowly down the lane. John looked back briefly and waved to his mother, who stood in the open door outlined by the glow of the light behind her.

There had been other bear hunts. John could no longer recall the age at which he had first gone with his father and the hounds. Every winter since then, he had spent days running behind the hounds or waiting silently on stand in the hope that he would get a good shot at a bear. And John still had not killed his first bear.

Generations of hunters before him had been drawn from the warmth of home fires to the discomforts of the hunt. And before them, the Indians in these mountains experienced the same excitement pursuing the lumbering bears that lived in the forest. A boy could kill a deer and put venison on the family table, and feel like a man doing it. But the hunter who kills his first bear feels himself to be a giant. There was no need for John to speak with his father of these thoughts as they jolted along with their truck and their pack.

Eldon Jones's famous Bear Mountain Lodge always seemed to be filled with eager, laughing hunters at this season. Some of them traveled from distant states for the hunts and joined the local mountain men in pursuit of both bear and the wild Russian hogs that roamed the hills. In the rush season Eldon sometimes called in extra guides, and his first choice was Luther, who knew as much about bears and their habits as most men would like to know. And for Luther the hunts were an opportunity to add to the family income by doing what he most liked to do.

"I'm booked to the rafters for next week," Jones had told him. "Can you come over for the three-day hunt?"

"I can if you'll let me bring my boy, John," Luther answered. "John's a good one in the woods. He could help me out, and maybe do some hunting too."

"You do that," Jones had said quickly. "We'll need all the guns we can get."

After two hours Luther's truck entered the graveled side road to Bear Mountain Lodge. The parking lot seemed to be filled with cars and the big main room of the lodge was crowded. "There are six hunters to go with you tomorrow," Eldon Jones told Luther. "What do you think of that area around Briartop Mountain stretching over toward Goat Bald, and between there and Bee Sting Creek?"

Luther knew the country well, although he had last hunted it three years ago. There were rich feeding areas of beech and oak on the lower altitudes and laurel thickets that covered great areas of the mountain high near the ridge.

"Fine," he said, "that's mighty good bear country. If I was a bear I'd live up there—either there or in the national park eating cookies."

For bear hunters, morning seems to come in the middle of the night. Far ahead of the first hint of dawn the lodge was bustling and the smell of scrambled eggs, crisp bacon, and hot coffee was everywhere. Then the men were loading their guns and dogs, and soon Luther's party was off to Briartop Mountain, to the north. Eventually they turned from the forest road and jolted along rutted and seldom-used logging trails.

John stood in the early light with his back against a great hemlock tree in a little saddle of the ridge. An animal coming up the mountain would provide him a shot for a considerable distance. His father had picked this spot well.

Somewhere off on either side of him stood other hunters, like sentinels guarding the mountaintop. Luther had gone with the hounds far down the slope. "If I can locate the feeding places," he explained, "the dogs will pick up the trail. Both the bears and the boars will bed in the laurel thickets. And if we can get 'em out of bed and running, we'll try to start 'em up over the mountain toward you."

Several miles below, Luther turned onto a new trail and followed the creek bed down the narrow, twisting valley.

An hour passed, and then another. So silently had John stood that a grouse came from the underbrush and walked in front of him a dozen feet away. The shy and skittish bird stopped within full view, scratched beneath the leaves, then walked on. A chickadee, alert to all that is strange in his tiny world, discovered John. The small gray creature with its light underside and black skull cap flew to a tiny branch above the boy's head and rocked there scolding the intruder. Then down the side of the mountain a doe walked into the forest clearing and eventually wandered from sight, unaware that she had been observed.

In late afternoon, John's fingers were stiff with cold.

He flexed them to keep the blood circulating and doubled his fist inside his gloves. He fingered the trigger of his gun to reassure himself that he knew its position if the need should come. He even released the safety on his rifle once to see how loud the click might sound, then put the safety back in position. He had stood longer than a young hunter could be expected to stand, unless he had grown up in the woods and understood the ways of the creatures there. Then he heard the voices of the hounds on the slopes far below.

Old Nan was first, as John had expected. Then came Prince and Billy to join the concert. Ripper, the half-airedale attack dog, never did give voice. John forgot that his fingers were stiff with the cold—suddenly he felt warm all over. The chase was angling along the great slope.

He listened carefully to the tone and the style of the dogs' barking. This, he hoped, was a bear and not a boar. And the trail was hot because the hounds neither slackened their pace nor ceased their barking. John strained his eyes to see down the mountainside.

When he first saw the bear, he thought the animal was heading directly toward his stand. "Give him another minute or so," John whispered to himself as he began to bring the gun to his shoulder. At this moment, however, the bear veered to the north and ran parallel to the ridge. The hounds came close behind, and John could pick them out individually even at this distance.

The animals, bear and hounds alike, were quickly

out of sight. In a matter of seconds they had emerged from the underbrush and returned to it. With them went John's chance of getting a shot. The animal headed along the ridge.

John heard a change in the dogs' barking. He started running through the woods; the hounds had the bear treed. Then he heard the sharp report of a rifle. The bear was on the ground when John arrived.

Darkness was coming, and soon after the bear was loaded onto the back of Luther's pickup, the party wound its way down the mountainside again toward the lodge.

Beyond the ridge of the mountain to the west, Nick awakened from his deep slumber. He had spent the day near the head of a small hollow choked with tangled undergrowth and carpeted with an accumulation of leafmold.

In the growing darkness, he rose from his bed, tested the air, and listened to the forest sounds. Then he moved off toward the top of the ridge. He crossed the mountaintop and started down the slope into the area hunted that day by Luther's party. He spent much of the night feeding beneath the beech trees and the oaks. Twice he came upon the scent of the hounds. Each time he growled and lifted his head to test the air, then stood on his hind feet to investigate further.

He found the place where the trail of the hounds and the smaller bear came together. He followed the trail upward for a short distance and then tested the air

161

again. Eventually, he left this evidence and resumed his search for food.

Toward morning, at an elevation of forty-five hundred feet, he came to the laurel thickets. He forced his way into the jungle of stems and branches, wedged his body through the dense heart of the tangle, and lay down in a pile of leaves among the roots.

Meanwhile, lights were being turned on in the hunting lodge and John and Luther Swope were silently pulling on their hunting clothes and preparing for the second day of the hunt. "I have a feelin' we should go back to the same place," Luther told Eldon Jones after breakfast. "The bears may be movin' there. Also, it's as good a place as any to get up some hogs."

His full belly and deep sleep had fogged Nick's mind, but the yelling of the Swope hounds promptly brought him to full alertness. Somewhere below, dogs were unraveling his trail. He sat up in his bed and listened. Holding his head high, he sniffed first to one side then the other. The air was still, but his ears told him the story with growing clarity.

Nick's massive shoulders forced the undergrowth aside as he worked his way to the uphill side of the laurel thicket. Here the dogs would have extreme difficulty traveling. Bears and boars and small creatures could find their way through laurel tangles, but dogs surrounded by the relentless force of the vegetation sometimes became so entangled they howled in rage and fear. Nick would feel safer, however, out in the more open forest. Although he seldom climbed any more, his mother had taught him long ago the value of taking refuge in the trees. And experience had shown him that, if he must, he could leap down among the dogs and beat them mercilessly with his paws until they were dead or scared off. He reached the uphill edge of the thicket after winding circuitously through its heart for a quarter of an hour. Steadily the sound of the yapping hounds came closer. They were following every step of his journey of the night before. He had not come by the shortest distance, but had instead made uncounted little side trips in search of food. Now the hounds had the task of tracing out each of these trails and coming at last to where the bear had slept.

They came to the lower edge of the vast laurel thicket that spread across acres of Briartop Mountain's rocky, timbered slope.

John could hear the hounds in the distance. Their voices said "bear," and once again he forgot all the cold and discomforts in his excitement.

Somewhere far below the hounds worked through the laurel. John realized that the animal was coming on at an angle that should bring it out to the top of the ridge very close to his stand.

Then he saw the vibrating saplings against which the creature was rubbing in its haste to escape the hounds. There was a great patch of black and a quick view of the bear, as big as any bear he had ever seen. John's hands trembled on the rifle. An instant later a monstrous creature was out of the laurel running at full speed toward the open timber, presenting John with a perfect broadside shot at less than a hundred yards.

Nick turned slightly uphill, and for a long moment John had him solidly in the sights of his rifle. Smoothly, the muzzle of the rifle followed the black form. "Now," he told himself. But for a reason he could not explain, his finger did not obey the command to squeeze. The bear galloped closer, until scarcely forty feet separated him from the tall, slender mountain youth looking at him down the long barrel of the rifle.

This magnificent bear, running at full speed, almost imperceptibly favored his right front foot. There was a nagging doubt in John's mind. If any man owned this bear, it perhaps should have been John. But he began to understand that no man owns any wild creature of the woods or fields or streams. Man shares the world with all its creatures, and takes what he needs to survive, just as other creatures take their living. What would he do with the body of this beast? He could pull the trigger and, once more, possess the body, but not the spirit—the wild spirit—that made Nick the symbol of all wild creatures.

John did not overestimate the praise and acclaim he would have reaped by taking the massive bear into his possession. With one easy shot he could have captured for himself the record for the biggest bear in many years.

But now Nick had loped out of sight, and John was

glad the temptation was gone. Perhaps there would be other bears at other times, but this was between Nick and the boy, and Nick had gone his way unaware of his great danger.

John knew that there was at least one more hunter on this side of the ridge, and even as he thought about it, there came the sharp report of a heavy rifle. Then the second shot rang out, and a third. The hunter was doing too much shooting. John ran to the top of the ridge. There he found Mr. Brenshaw, for once so excited he could hardly speak coherently. He babbled about a giant bear for several minutes before his words became clear. "John," he said, "I've seen big bears, mostly in zoos where they're fed too much, but this one looked big as a buffalo romping off through the woods. And I'm not ashamed to admit I got so nervous I forgot everything I ever knew about shooting. Now nobody will believe me when I tell them how big that bear was."

"Maybe they will, Mr. Brenshaw," John said quietly. "I believe you."

Chapter
20

*T**he warm air of spring felt good to Nick. As bears* go he was now, in his tenth year, middle-aged. But the rigors of his life had taxed his body. He was feeling occasional signs of advancing age before his time. The troublesome tooth, the aching muscles were constantly with him, robbing him of sleep and sometimes of the speed and strength he had once known. With each day he felt increasingly eager to move on—to the ridges on the horizon and down the slopes on the far side. He followed this urge that he did not understand.

A few evenings later he came to a campground that brought memories. The tables and the buildings were familiar, as was the gurgling cold creek with its little foot bridge. But the automobiles and tents and the people with food had not yet come.

At the boundary of the park Nick stood on the

wooded slope across the valley from the little farms of Luther Swope and his neighbor.

Shortly after daylight the next morning the Swopes were at their breakfast table when an aging car bumped up the drive and slid to a stop. The kitchen door shook and rattled to the pounding of Herb Gordon's sledge-hammer fist. "Luther! Anybody home?"

Herb stood in the kitchen just inside the door, half yelling about the cursed bears and how time had come to do away with the lot of them. Gordon's face was flushed red and his hands were waving up and down as if he were trying to sell something at an auction.

John's mother poured Herb a cup of coffee and the man waved it aside. "Ain't got time for visitin'," he said, "but I thank you. I got to get after that bear. Luther, I swear a bear the size of that one could take all of us."

"Herb," said Luther quietly, "what bear?"

"The one I saw killin' my sheep this morning," Herb said. "Caught the thievin' beast right at the scene of his crime. And if you'll give me the loan of your dogs I'll get him maybe before he can get back to the park. I just saw him five minutes ago, right before I came over here. You want to come and bring the dogs?"

The truth was that Luther was not eager to join Gordon in pursuit of this bear. He did not like to release his hounds so close to the national park boundary and take a chance on their going into the park and maybe killing one of those protected bears. You couldn't blame

167

dogs for that. They had no way of knowing where the park boundary lay.

But there was also the matter of neighborliness. "John, why don't you take two of the hounds on the chains. Take 'em over to Mr. Gordon's and see if they can pick up the trail. And if they do, then pull 'em off. Take them and make a big circle with them and see if they can find a trail of this bear coming out of the park. That way we can run him toward Mr. Gordon's place, and I can stay here in case he comes through our place. We won't be running game toward the park and we can get the hounds back too."

Gordon shook his head in admiration. He was beginning to calm down. The situation might shape up better than he had ever hoped. "Luther," he said now, "I always did say you was the best bear man in these hills."

Luther did not answer.

If Gordon had observed the evidence in his pasture field more carefully, and had reported it truthfully, Luther might not have aided him at all in this hunt. Gordon knew only that he saw a bear eating a freshly killed sheep. He did not know of the tangled events leading up to that moment in the gray light of early dawn.

During the night a band of free-running hounds had been chasing through the countryside in pursuit of whatever creatures, wild or domestic, they might encounter. One among them was a black and tan, mean with age and ill treatment. When the old hound was home during the day, he slept in the dust beneath Herb

Gordon's house. But at night he roamed. Herb had raised him from a pup, the only hound he kept these days.

In the company of five other dogs Gordon's hound came late in the night toward his home place. In daytime around the house the old black and tan was docile and knew how to keep out of Herb's way. But the darkness of night and the company of other hounds bolstered his courage.

This pack came to Gordon's line fence and wiggled through the wires into the sheep lot. They were trailing silently across the lot when the little band of two dozen sheep headed out on a full run away from them. With the cunning of their wild ancestors the hounds cut from the pack a heavy ewe who lagged a few feet behind.

One of the hounds lunged at her neck while Gordon's own black and tan clamped onto a rear leg and helped drag her down. The sheep was soon dead and the dogs began to feed, completely unaware that, at this moment, a creature far larger than any of them had come onto the scene.

A full night of roaming and hunting through the woods had left the great bear with his hunger still unsatisfied. If he had fed well he would by this hour have found a place to bed down for the coming day. But he came instead to the edge of the woods and stood there— a great dark bulk in the world of shadows.

He heard the gentle moving of the sheep off to his right and in the middle of the pasture. The soft breeze was in his face and he studied the smells it carried.

But he was attracted by the sounds. A pack of dogs had broken from the night, and the bear heard the thudding of the sheeps' hoofs as they raced in panic before the hounds. An ordinary bear might at this point have retreated quietly into the timberlands from which he had come. He might have avoided all risk of trouble, as most wild creatures do by nature.

This bear, however, had come to understand the power of his muscles and appreciate the bargaining force of his teeth and claws. Over the years he had developed a sense of independence. Nick knew he was an invincible giant among the wild creatures of the mountains.

Instead of rushing either into or away from the action, he waited. His eyesight gave him few clues about the progress of the chase, but his ears and his nose carried the story to him in minute detail. He knew when the hounds had cut their animal from the flock and, by their growling, he knew when the kill was made. This was his cue.

So intent were the hounds on their meal that the hulking beast was almost among them before they sensed his presence. The hounds fell back and formed a snarling half circle on the far side of the sheep's carcass. Two of the hounds quickly dashed out to distract the bear, as they sometimes did with other creatures. The first of them collided with a bear's paw as big as a washpan. It descended out of the dark with deadly, practiced

170

aim, and crushed and tore him brutally. There was not even sufficient time for one final scream. The second hound fell back among the others, and they made short, halfhearted feints toward the bear. They had chased and cornered other bears, both inside and outside the park, but never had they encountered a bear such as this one.

Nick, however, had not come here to kill hounds. For that matter he had not come here to kill sheep. But, being a bear, he recognized opportunity when it presented itself. Now, as if ignoring the dogs, he advanced to the dead sheep.

This was too much for the hounds to tolerate. They had hunted all night and now were driven to desperation by the sight of having food which they had claimed suddenly taken from them. One of them secured a grip on the flesh of the bear's rear leg. The bear turned on the hound and missed him. When the hound released his grip, the bear dashed after the retreating dog. By then the remaining hounds had seized this opportunity and closed in from the rear.

Nick turned on the three hounds behind him and again the single hound attacked. Rage swept over the bear and with a deep growl he pronounced the doom of this persistent, detested creature who attacked him from the rear. With a sudden recovery of his youthful reactions he turned at spring-steel speed and in the same motion felt the head and side of the dog make contact with his paw. With an extra surge of force he ripped the hound, who now became the second victim to fall on this battlefield in the brief and bloody predawn battle.

Now the bear put one of his paws on the back of still another hound. But instead of killing him with his claws he held the squirming dog in both arms and, opening his cavernous mouth as far as he could, Nick bit through the creature's neck.

The two remaining hounds, including Gordon's rangy black and tan, ran with their tails between their legs toward the woods.

With the dogs gone, the bear picked up the carcass of the sheep and started carrying it off in the direction of the woods, where he could lie down and eat at his leisure. But Herb Gordon, aroused by the barking, had arrived. He saw a huge black bear trotting toward the woods with one of his sheep.

When John brought the two Plotts hounds to Gordon's field, the dead sheep still lay where the bear had dropped it. In recent years, John had looked almost automatically at the print of every bear he encountered, searching for one with two toes missing. He searched now for the tracks left by the "killer" bear. He dropped to one knee and studied the ground. "Nan, Bill," he said quietly, "let's go." The eager dogs pulled him away into the woods, leaving Gordon standing guard in the pasture field with his shotgun.

To adhere to the plan his father had outlined, John should have pulled the hounds from the trail of the bear

172

and begun making a great circle around to the border of the park. But through his mind flashed the picture of the old black bear, a giant now, a bear that started out as a spunky cub and never let the world change him completely. And he thought next of Herb Gordon. Then the two pictures came together, as if superimposed, and John could see Gordon shooting Nick, then gloating over the carcass. He would see that the whole county knew he had shot the biggest bear in the mountains.

Instead of turning from the trail, John let the hounds stick tight to it. He snapped the chains together behind him and the straining dogs dragged him forward through the woods.

The trail led in a succession of turns and little side trips down through the timber to Spicer Creek. Then it headed directly up the other mountain. Now John could almost predict the exact spot where Nick had come out of the park. By the time John reached the park border, he was sweating and fighting for breath. John's legs were long now, but it had been an uphill run from Spicer Creek and so he tied the dogs to a redbud tree and sat down for a rest before starting back.

Instead of going back to Gordon's place, John turned westward. He wanted to consult with his father. "Pa," he said, "I didn't do it the way you told me. I didn't take the dogs off the trail."

"You mean," his father said, "that you let a stock-killing bear run right back to the park?"

"That bear was Nick. He's back. I saw his tracks."

"John, if Nick's a stock killer that's all there is to it! He's no different from any other bear in that case. Next time he may come back for our stock, or somebody else's besides Gordon's. A stock-killing bear doesn't change his habits."

"I'm not sure," John said. "Maybe he didn't kill that sheep." Luther stopped in his work and looked up at his son. "It wasn't full daylight yet, and I didn't have time to study it right, but there were some mighty strange marks around that pasture of Mr. Gordon's. The way I read it there's more mixed up in that killing than just one bear and one sheep. That's why I came back here first. I wanted you to go look at the tracks."

They found Gordon at his barn. He was still leaning against the corner of the building with his shotgun beside him. "Johnny," he said, "I figured you to come back this way."

"I just never did get that bear headed back in your direction," John said. He decided to explain it no further.

"I thought maybe we should have a look around your field, Herb," Luther said. "Maybe we can see what really did happen."

"I can tell you right quick what really did happen," said Gordon. His face was getting red again and his anger growing. "A big stock-killin' bear came right into my pasture and killed one of my sheep. That's what happened. Any question about that, and you can go look at the sheep. John's already seen it. And I figure if I hadn't

175

showed up when I did, that bear would have killed the whole flock of them. I tell you we've got to kill that bear. Then we've got to kill all the other bears we can kill. One's as bad as the next, and if one hasn't killed stock already it's just a matter of time 'till he gets around to it."

They walked out to the carcass of the sheep. John and his father began a careful study of the tracks. There were the tracks of the bear and tracks John and Gordon had made. But there were no other tracks. "That means he carried the sheep away," said Luther.

"That's what I've been trying to tell you, Luther. He carried the sheep off just like it was his own."

"But I want to see where from." Luther began back-tracking the bear carefully. He found occasional prints in the dust and here and there, places where the weeds were pushed down by the animal's weight. Herb Gordon and John had trouble following him now, as he led them directly to the scene over the little knoll where the field was scuffed like a corral. Here they found the ripped bodies of the three strange hounds.

"I told you that bear's a real killer," Gordon was more excited now than ever. "He killed them dogs too."

Luther looked at him for some time. "What," he asked, "do you suppose those hounds were up to?"

Gordon paused for only a moment. "I expect they was tryin' to chase the bear away," he said. "You know hounds will fight bears every chance they get."

John and his father were still studying the ground for clues of the early morning's events. They found the trail of the band of sheep and in one place the footprints of the large dogs running close beside them. Then they found Nick's trail from the woods toward the place where the sheep was killed.

As he walked to the house, Gordon was still insisting that bears were the real troublemakers. "I'm going to kill every one I get the chance at," he said. In this he was promising no more and no less than practically every other man in the mountains. Since they had first come here to share the wilderness, men had waged relentless war on the native bears, who sometimes took what the men wanted for themselves. Earlier generations of Gordons and Swopes had taken bears in every imaginable manner. They had smoked them out of caves with smudge fires. They had built heavy logs into deadfalls and enticed the bears into these crushing devices with the carcass of a deer or hog. Some men even rigged shotguns to trees with the muzzles pointing across the trails, and strings tied to the triggers. This device killed many a bear and, now and then, a man who bumped against the string in the dimly lighted forest.

In his anger, Gordon couldn't resist a chance to taunt Luther. "I'm a little surprised," said Gordon now, "that your champion bear dogs couldn't set that killer back toward me. The trail was sure fresh enough. It kinda sets a man to wondering how good those hounds really are."

177

Luther controlled his sudden urge to send his fist smashing into the pudgy red face of his neighbor. "How many good dogs you got around here?" he asked.

"You know I don't keep any dogs to amount to anything. Only got one old harmless black and tan. And I only keep him out of sentiment."

"Well," said Luther, "I'll tell you what you do the very next time you got bear troubles, you get your old black and tan and you take off with him after that bear. You don't seem to have faith in my dogs any more, so I expect there wouldn't be much reason for you to come asking me favors with them." John knew his father was still angry enough to fight. A man can talk about some things, but as his father once told him, "No insult is worse than faulting another man's dogs."

"I'll tell you something else," he said as he climbed into the truck. "If you got any sheep needs killing, you might try your black and tan on them. I just got a feeling he'd know how to go about it." The Swope pickup threw gravel behind it on the way out of the driveway.

Chapter
21

One *ne night the next summer Nick wandered again* through the woodlands in a westerly direction. He eased along the top of the rock ledge where his mother had taken him as a cub. He rounded the end of the cliff and turned down the long incline to Spicer Creek. He waded the creek and headed up through the woods toward Swope's.

At the edge of the clearing beyond the barn with its tobacco stripping shed, Nick stopped and looked around. There were no lights. Even the hounds were silent this night. Now the bear slipped along the weedy edge of the little clearing and came around the corner of the barn. He went to the bee hives.

Nick sniffed the base of the hives and the insects, disturbed, increased the tempo of their buzzing. Casually he put out one paw and tested the wooden boxes. He reached then to the top of a hive and tilted it until it fell over on the grass. Frenzied bees swarmed around his head but Nick ignored their buzzing and their efforts to sting him. One or two stung him on the nose but he simply stuck his nose deeper into the honey, which was now running from the crushed combs.

The clatter of the falling hive alerted Swope's hounds and the night came alive with their yapping. Luther climbed from bed, took the shotgun from behind the door, and picked up his powerful coon-hunting light.

Nick heard the door bang and saw the flash of light. He ran back across the barnyard and gained speed as he galloped down the hill and into the woods, straight for the park.

At breakfast the next morning Luther discussed the bear damage with John. "After chores," he said, "you take the dogs, keep 'em on the chains and see if you can find where that bear went. If he didn't go inside the park again—and I'll bet he did—we might put an end to his thieving ways."

With two of the hounds jerking at their chains and barking loudly, John searched for tracks of the bear. He found them in the soft earth along the edge of the barnyard and he knelt down for a closer look. "Nick," he said quietly. "Nick, you old devil! I wish you'd learn a thing or two. You're going to get it yet, sure as cats have kittens."

A decade had passed since John had kept this bear in the stripping shed. Both the boy and the bear had grown big. John could not erase the uneasy thought from his mind that he too might be partly responsible for Nick's troubles, for he knew that a bear can not go on forever getting in and out of man-trouble without meeting his executioner.

Once bears had found their lives bounded only by the forces of nature. There were storms, disease, hunger, and fire. But if these forces changed the species, it was by removing the individuals unable to withstand the rigors of the black bear's environment. The loss of the individual was not a tragedy to the species, and the world of the black bears went on with each new century as it had in the centuries past.

Then, men had come and drawn a line around the ridges and slopes of these sprawling mountains and marked the boundaries of the great nationl park. Here all creatures were said to be safe. But the park's protected bears met a more subtle and sinister threat. Some of them accepted the welfare offerings of park visitors and sacrificed their independence.

The frantic hounds strained at the chains and jerked at John as he studied the tracks. After two hundred yards of trailing there was no longer any doubt about the direction the bear had gone. The dogs could not know what John now knew for certain: the bear was safe inside the national park.

And if big Nick had treed or stopped short of the park boundary, John would just as soon not find out. He pulled the hounds from the trail. "Went straight for the park," John told his father. "I reckon he won't be back for a while."

"Maybe not until tonight anyhow," Luther said.

After he came in from the field that evening, John took the pickup and drove off toward the park. He passed several carloads of tourists on the steep mountain road and this traffic slowed him down. For four miles he inched the truck up the twisting blacktop highway toward the mountain top.

As he expected, the parking lot at the picnic grounds was filled with cars. He stopped too when he saw the size of the bear. Nick sat on his haunches. His eyes roved from one person to the next, his face was expressionless.

As John watched, a man in shorts and a brilliant red and yellow sport shirt moved toward the bear. He held an 8mm movie camera to his eye, and the machine made a steady whirring noise to which big Nick was long accustomed. He was not, however, accustomed to having a camera moved to within two feet of his nose. The bear dropped to all four feet and moved farther back. The crowd pressed after him and closed in once more around this wonderfully amusing black bear that would figure so heavily in their stories back home during the coming months.

The man with the camera came in again. "He needs to do something," he called to his wife, "to make it a good picture." The woman handed her husband a cookie and he tossed it to the bear. As Nick bent and picked the cookie from the ground the camera whirred some more. "Now you go feed him one," the man said.

"I'm not going close to that thing," his wife announced.

"He's not going to hurt you." Her husband acted half angry. "These bears know people."

The woman walked, one slow step at a time, holding the cookie at arm's length in a trembling, well-manicured hand. Finally, she tossed the cookie to the animal and backed quickly off. Her husband shook his head. "Don't know how you expect a man to get good movies."

Big Nick's glinting eyes stared into the face of the angry man, weighing every move he made. Nick saw the man remove a small red object from his pocket and take a shiny thing from his other pocket. "You have to have action," said the man, "to make good movies."

As the man held a lighter to the fuse of the firecracker, a tall youth dressed in blue-denim work clothes pushed through the crowd and towered over the man. It happened so rapidly that the moviemaker jumped with alarm. "Don't do that," the boy said distinctly, and loud enough now for all the suddenly silent crowd to hear. John's eyes were narrowed. His lips formed a grim tight line. With a lightning-fast motion of his hand, John reached for the lighted firecracker. He grabbed it from the man, who pushed backward now through the crowd. John followed. At the final moment before the lighted fuse burned to the powder, John flipped the firecracker casually at the feet of the moviemaker.

183

As the firecracker exploded, the moviemaker stumbled. Muttering, he scrambled to his feet and ran to his car. An approving murmur spread through the crowd.

Now John turned to the bear, which had begun walking toward the woods. There was something strange going on here, and the unfamiliar always made Nick suspicious. Alert to danger, he had forgotten his hunger.

Nick turned half around and stood looking at John. Ten feet of distance separated the boy and the bear. The old bear lifted his nose to test the air. He turned his head first one way, then the other. John wondered suddenly if it were possible for a bear to remember this long. He would never know for certain. But the old bear looked at him again, looked very closely.

The crowd was returning, curious about this mountain youth and the big bear. John, suddenly self-conscious in front of all these strangers, advanced a step or two on the bear. He waved his hands as a person might to chase chickens from the garden patch. "Go on," he said to the bear. "Go on, Nick, get out of here. Get back to the woods where you belong."

The ranger arrived in his green truck as John backed around and turned onto the highway. The ranger recognized him and waved. John waved back, smiled, and drove away.

"You shoulda been here a while ago."

"Why's that?" the ranger asked.

"Guy tried to feed a bear a firecracker so he could get a movie of what the bear did."

"Anybody get his license number?" the ranger asked. No one had.

The ranger walked across the picnic ground. He looked carefully in the dust and pointed at the bear tracks. "It's a wonder," he said seriously, "that bear didn't mangle him for a stunt like that. See those tracks? That was old Three Toes. He's a mighty independent character. He's caused us trouble before. We've even trapped him and hauled him away once, but he came back. It's a matter of time. He gets into trouble again and we won't have any choice. We'll have to shoot him.

"That's strange," said a man with binoculars hanging from his neck. "You say the bear's name is Three Toes? That young man who left in the pickup was the one kept the man from giving the bear the firecracker. I thought he was planning to make the guy eat that firecracker. Then he chased that big bear off into the woods. But he didn't call him what you called him. He called him Nick. He said, 'Go on Nick, get back to the woods where you belong.'"

THE AUTHOR

George Laycock grew up on a farm near Zanesville, Ohio, and studied wildlife management at Ohio State University. After graduation he joined the staff of *Farm Quarterly* as associate editor, but resigned in 1951 to devote his full time to writing. His articles have appeared in *Country Gentlemen, Sports Illustrated, Better Homes and Gardens, Field and Stream, Outdoor Life,* and *Sports Afield.* A number of his articles have been illustrated with his own photographs. Mr. Laycock has traveled over much of North and South America, observing animals in their natural habitats. His other children's books are: *Never Pet a Porcupine, Never Trust a Cowbird,* and *Whitetail: The Story of a White-tailed Deer.* He lives in Cincinnati, Ohio, with his wife and three children.

THE ARTIST

Nancy Grossman was born in New York City and is a graduate of Pratt Institute. At twenty-six she has had three one-man shows of her paintings and collages, and she was the recent recipient of a Guggenheim Fellowship. Her book illustration includes *Far Out the Long Canal,* by Meindert DeJong, *Evan's Corner,* by Elizabeth Starr Hill, and *Aboard the Lizzie Ross,* by Harriet Vaughan Davies. Miss Grossman lives in New York City.